YOUTH PEACE COLLECTIVE

by Janet Zoglin

To Mayor Manny Diaz –
Con todo respeto, tienes
tu lugarcito en mi libro, mi Alcalde
(p. 123)
Thank you for being part
of my vision for
world peace

Outskirts Press
Denver, Colorado

HAPPY HOLIDAYS
Janet Zoglin
12/03

This is a work of fiction. The events described here are imaginary. Some well-known public figures appear in fictional settings.

Youth Peace Collective

Outskirts Press
http://www.outskirtspress.com

ISBN: 0-9725874-6-2

Outskirts Press and the "OP" logo are trademarks belonging to On the Outskirts, Inc.

Printed in the United States of America

For my Parents
and
my Brothers, including T.

and in memory of

M. Friedson and M. Lenihan

CONTENTS

ACKNOWLEDGMENTS

I wish to thank Jeni for logos, book cover and overall manuscript assistance; Schil for unique art work; Sarah for the laptop; Walt for computer backup; Manuel for his internet cafe; Sophia, Steven and Lisa for Ghana descriptions; Susan for Palestine realism; Deb, for her knowledge of Amma; Oliver for listening to me read chapters; and the Mendible Family, for always being there.

I would also like to remember my friend, the late Luis Sanjurjo, who told me many, many years ago, "Write if you have to."

peace (pēs) *n.* 1. freedom from war or civil disorder. 2. a contract to end war. 3. harmony in human relations. 4. tranquillity; quietness

The New American Webster
Handy College Dictionary

INTRODUCTION

On April 7, 2003, in the midst of the war in Iraq and my writing of this book, the Miami Herald published an article in a section titled "Journal from the Front," by Meg Laughlin. This particular story was called "Soldiers take needed timeout for a good deed," and it described American soldiers from the Army's V Corps, 7th CSG (a combat support group) deciding to take a 500-gallon tank of potable water and 100 pounds of rice to a village where U.S. shelling had destroyed the town water pump. The story recounts the soldiers' ride to the village through a landscape littered with empty multiple-launching rocket pods, toppled mud-brick homes, piles of rubble, abandoned fields of crops, and burned out vehicles. It tells of the villagers' initial fear, and how they eventually brought whatever containers they could find to collect water from the three spigots on the tank. The "town elder" invites the five soldiers into his dirt-floor house, where they drink hot, sweet black tea and eat homemade pita with cinnamon that villagers give them, their gas masks, helmets and M-16 rifles set aside on a red rug. The elder quotes the Koran saying God watches over those who have and those who have not, and we all deserve his love and protection. As the soldiers leave they put their hands over their hearts and bow, following the Islamic way of showing respect. In the final quote, by a Staff Sergeant from Long Island, the soldier states that now he has done something that feels good, because you don't feel good when you're killing people. How curious, I thought, that in the midst of the war, a soldier would actually be quoted making such a telling statement. War is inherently about killing, and it doesn't feel good to the people who have to do it.

Youth Peace Collective is about the opposite of war. It is about trying to take the world we face today, and transform it into a place which is motivated by the desire to help and construct, not to hurt and destroy. This book exists because the organization does not; we were not able to acquire start-up funding. If we had, the following story is what I believe might have occurred. Though it is a work of fiction about peace, these pages contain many actual experiences, visions, and ideas. The names of most adults are real, including some well known public figures portrayed in fictional settings. Names of all youth have been changed to protect their innocence. For they are innocent. They are not the ones who created this world of violence, but they have inherited it. Every day it becomes increasingly clear to me that it is our responsibility, the adults of this world, to present a different alternative to future generations.

Readers, allow me to share my blueprint for making war obsolete. Please believe that it is possible.

Janet Zoglin
August, 2003
Miami

Chapter 1

Out of frustration, an idea is born

The idea came to me the summer of 2000 on the fire escape of my brother's apartment in the East 30's of New York City. Each night I sat there thinking, after spending my days trying to develop a shelter for homeless 18-23 year olds. My brother was out of town; I was subletting his place.

Actually, the idea wheels were set in motion the stroke of midnight that famous turn of the millennium, January 2000, while Oliver and I looked out my window on the third floor of the Tower Hotel in Little Havana, Miami. We each had rented a room there, on a monthly basis, and were both unemployed. He's my dear friend since '94 when we were counselors and outreach partners for Streetwork, a program in Manhattan working with street-involved youth. We found ourselves, that instant when Y2k did not happen (personally, I was disappointed, believing we were about to experience world transformation), watching fireworks in the eastern sky, set off from South Beach. A week later I flew to the Midwest to help my parents, both of whom had strokes, my father's the previous November extremely serious. After two months in the hospital, he was being released, and I went to assist his re-entry home. When I returned to Miami the beginning of February, Oliver was with me as I played my answering machine messages.

We heard the voice of Angela, Streetwork's former Clinical Director but by then overall Director, asking if

I was interested in a three to six month job creating a shelter from scratch. Her words held exactly the correct lure: a short-term time frame and a project starting something new. I spent March with my parents and began working the first of April. Oliver stayed in Miami a few more months, then left for San Francisco.

So, every night that summer of 2000 was spent in contemplation on my brother's fire escape. Already in June it was clear to me the three to six month time projection was a dream. I had contacted over 100 social service agencies, churches, synagogues, and various and sundry individuals looking for space, initially on the Lower East Side but ultimately ANYWHERE in the City, that we could "share," but no one had an inch to spare. We convinced our funder, HOPWA (Housing Opportunities for Persons with AIDS), to let us modify our project proposal and write in costs for renting space. By July every hope had gone sour – a two story office building in "El Barrio" of East Harlem we discovered had an illegal wood addition; a half-way house for men out of prison offering us a wing of their facility was suddenly defunded and had to close; and the welfare hotel on Central Park North that Angela said nobody, "not even you," could make warm and homey enough for the kids. With no other options, we were considering leasing a large apartment in the Harlem area, around Broadway and 149th, when miraculously, in mid-August, the good people of St. Luke AME Church on upper Amsterdam showed us their parsonage, which was for rent. Enveloped in sweat and frustration, one of those steamy nights, the idea of the Youth Peace Collective came to my stressed out mind.

Chapter 2

The Concept Paper
Tedious, but essential

Maybe even The Lanes, a youth run bowling alley and recreation center, came to me first, followed by Cooperation House, then the Youth Peace Collective. My immediate goal, developing a 15-bed emergency shelter, seemed like inordinate energy for a band-aid solution. I wanted to create something with more permanent results, to offer life changing opportunities to the youth I had worked with for so many years – a project based on a living model of peace.

Initially my idea was named Youth Peace Force, until Lucius Walker (of Pastors for Peace fame) said he was uncomfortable with the word "force." He felt it indicated domination and power over others. Of course, he wasn't from the "May the Force be with you" generation, but I gave it thought and after hours of word searching, Oliver came up with "Collective," which was a good word, because that's what we are.

Rather than paraphrase the document, I wish to present the initial Concept Paper, in its entirety. Oliver and I developed it together, because the first one I wrote myself railed about American media, violence, greed, and sounded like a reprimand. Hopefully this will give you a clear picture of what we intend to do, since the concept paper was what we sent potential funders, along with a brochure and the logo my friend Jeni in Miami designed for us. Our brochure states: "Our Philosophy: The Youth Peace Collective believes that young adults desire to create a positive future for themselves and the world around them. In urban America many young people lack concrete options to better their lives and youth from developing countries have even fewer possibilities. We offer that opportunity through a cooperative living and working experience, on the job training, theoretical and practical skill building, and fair compensation. Our goal is to help transform the lives of youth from the U.S. and developing nations while bringing water infrastructure to countries in need. Our mission is building peace through commitment, service, and mutual respect."

YOUTH PEACE COLLECTIVE

The Concept

Peace is a way of life. The intention of the Youth Peace Collective (YPC) is to allow young people to train, work, live and receive financial compensation in an environment promoting harmonious relationships and nonviolence. Our organizational philosophy and operational style are egalitarian and non-hierarchical to provide a living model of working cooperatively. Youth will be able to experience the benefit of humanitarian efforts in their own lives and those of people around the world.

Individuals between the ages of 18-25, will be offered the chance to work for six months on a project building infrastructure in a developing country. The work will be physical labor with the specific goals of bringing clean, running water, effective sewage systems, and possibly irrigation, to a country lacking this basic structure. In host countries, YPC will provide

Collective members with room, board and a stipend, living in a democratically run community that they, along with counselors/staff, will set up, organize and self-govern. Collective members will attend workshops focused on technical skills, cooperative living and peace education. Upon completion of a six-month commitment, each person will receive $10,000 tax free, placed in a bank account in their home city. Youth from developing countries will earn an amount in their local currency and economy with the equivalent impact.

The Youth Peace Collective's main principle is: No violence of any kind. Youth members and staff will operate as collectives and decision-making will be done by consensus. All staff salaries will be equal, though there will be different delineations of tasks. Urban projects, such as The Lanes (youth run bowling alley) and Cooperation House (transitional and long-term, independent living housing) will be developed in U.S. cities to serve as training locations and continuing contact for participants.

Why is the Youth Peace Collective Necessary?

In the United States many young adults, particularly those from economically disadvantaged families, envision only limited options for their future. "Third World" youth see even fewer. Many teenagers have abandoned their education before completing high school, or if they do have a degree, hardly see a way to continue their education without taking on debt that would plague their lives for years to come. Young people are burdened by the pressure to "make money," perceiving that as the only road to achieving one's goals and improving life. For middle and upper class youth, that might mean pursuing careers in law, medicine, business, and finance. For children from welfare families, those with immigrant parents or immigrants themselves, ones who grew up in the foster system, spent time in jail or juvenile detention, whose caretakers were drug or alcohol addicted, this desire to "make money" may translate into illegal activities, due to the cycle of poverty. From an early age, Americans are surrounded by advertising and image-making, distancing them from the basics of survival and the healing aspects of helping other people. All over the developing world people feel trapped by the lack of economic mobility in their home countries. The Youth Peace Collective expects participants to work hard, improve the living conditions of individuals in need, actively engage in a democratically run youth-based community, learn the tools of building peace and be paid fairly for it. Through the participation of youth from host countries, a cultural exchange will take place enhancing the experience for all, providing a previously unachievable financial remuneration for citizens of underdeveloped nations. American youth will return to their homes after being involved in employment, training, and collective living in an environment radically different from the one they have known, expanding their vision for possibilities in a peaceful world. They will have the economic means to make a new start in life, in the direction of their choosing, after completing what will likely be a life transforming experience.

Organizational Structure and Application Procedure

The operational and administrative structures of the Youth Peace Collective will be horizontal, not vertical. Two basic collectives will exist -- the staff collective and the youth collective. The department divisions will be: administration, training, technical and community operations. One of the essential principles communicated on every level in the Youth Peace Collective is that no one is above anyone else or worth more. We are all inherently equal, possessing distinct talents and abilities we bring to the table. The application process will be simple – a two page form asking basic information and thought-provoking questions for the applicant to answer (in writing or audiotape). Each young person will have a personal interview with staff. The factors of desire to do the job and seriousness of commitment will exceed any elements in the youth's background. A medical examination will be necessary, with caution given to selection of youth with serious pre-existing conditions that could be exacerbated by working in difficult climates and conditions. Youth formerly incarcerated or involved with the justice system will not be precluded, in fact, they will be welcomed. The most important point that will be communicated to applicants is that no violent behavior, verbal, physical, emotional or sexual, will be tolerated in the Youth Peace Collective.

Administration

The Youth Peace Collective will have its headquarters in Miami, Florida. Regional offices will initially be established in the following locations: Philadelphia (Northeast); Atlanta (Southeast); Kansas City (Midwest); Albuquerque (Southwest) and Portland, Oregon (Northwest). Every host country will have an administrative office. Staff of the administrative offices will travel to locations in their region to do on-site interviews with potential candidates. The headquarters city and regional urban centers will be sites for the model projects of The Lanes and Cooperation House. Out of the administrative offices will come the back-up structure to help youth with application procedures, transportation, processing travel documents, medical issues, equipment and supply purchasing, and all traditionally fiscal and administrative tasks.

Training

Once a young person has completed his/her application, had a personal interview with staff, and been accepted into the Collective, that individual, in conjunction with staff, will determine when they enter training. The training period required for youth to go abroad will be one month long, offered during the three summer months. On-site trainings will take place as part of the Urban Projects for youth who desire to stay in the United States or have entered the Collective before the training period begins. Initially the location of training will possibly be the campus of a college or school that does not use its facility in the summer. Host country youth will train for one month at the host site. The training month is not calculated in the six-month work period, though youth will receive compensation at the end of any successfully completed training period, whether they join the Collective or not.

Training is the setting in which the group process begins, as well as detailed explanations and skill instruction on the types of tasks that will be involved in the Collective's work outside of the States. All of the concepts of self-government, egalitarian management, nonviolent conflict resolution, and mutual responsibility will be presented and practiced. Information about the host country, its culture and appropriate behavior for Collective members, as well as basic workshops on working cooperatively, mediation, power and oppression, peace education, and building healthy relationships will be an integral part of the program. In training, youth from all over the U.S., from different racial, ethnic, religious and economic groups, will be guided to develop the ability to work as a team. Each training session will participate in a "labor of peace" – a project of physical labor, carried out by the trainees, which will enhance some part of the infrastructure of the hosting facility. During the training period youth will get a clear sense of the maturity level, style of operation, and degree of seriousness that characterize the Youth Peace Collective.

Technical

The technical team will consist of American and host country engineers, architects, plumbers, electricians, agricultural and construction experts. Initially they will work in the host country, determining the technologies and logistics required to bring about an ecologically safe and economically viable system to create the infrastructure that is most needed. They will develop a work methodology and members of the technical team will be involved in training and orientation sessions to explain exactly how the task of creating the new infrastructure will come about. Any individuals who show particular interest and skill in the technical field may be assigned to specific technical placements which will involve additional, more highly specialized training.

Community Operations

An essential part of the Youth Peace Collective experience is working, living, and learning to make decisions by consensus with other Collective members. In the first year of operation, the design and expansion of the community will take place, constructing sleeping units, a dining hall, and other possibilities such as a "coffee house," music room, gym/exercise space, movie house, meditation room and sickbay. Task groups will be created in areas such as entertainment, sports, creativity, and wellness where collective members can come together and offer activities for the entire community. The first groups of collective members will also be determining the work hours, days, nature of tasks, and manner in which to organize work teams to bring about the infrastructure development. Tasks that maintain the community, such as food preparation, sanitation and cleanliness, laundry and security will be considered part of the work component. Four days a week will be devoted to work, and one day will be dedicated to workshops. Topics for the workshops will include non-aggressive communication, an examination of prejudice and discrimination, multi-cultural sensitivity, conflict resolution and many other topics to be generated by staff and youth participants. Additionally, sessions will be held on aspects of the history, geography, culture and political situation of the country in which the Youth Peace Collective is working. Collective members will have two days a week free from work, and besides the recreation facilities available in the main site, youth will be able to explore the surrounding communities. Drugs and alcohol will be prohibited in all Collective living areas and work locations. The system of government that the community sets up will determine how infractions of rules are dealt with. The staff in community operations will have a counselor/social worker mentality, operating under the harm reduction philosophy, believing that cooperation, respect, understanding and non-authoritarianism are the best means to achieve a productive, harmonious community.

Where would the Youth Peace Collective begin its work?

Presently the Youth Peace Collective has a site to develop a model project in Ghana, West Africa. Ultimately our model has the potential to be replicated all over the developing world. Ideal locations would be countries where there is a high level of un/underemployment for young adults and trained professionals and a recognized need for infrastructure development. Always mindful of the safety and security of Collective members, we would be cautious about entering countries in the midst of armed conflict or extreme societal violence. Wherever the Youth Peace Collective would work, we would have a positive impact on the local economy by creating a partnership towards improving local living conditions. In the host country, the mother (or caretaker/guardian of the Collective member) will receive the same compensation as the youth after each successful six-month commitment, thus assisting the entire extended family unit.

Benefits for All

Gearing the Youth Peace Collective to this age group is done for a very specific purpose. After adolescence, individuals are forming views and ideas on how to structure their adult lives – their minds are open and searching. Though full of energy and strength, they sometimes lack direction. By working and living in the Collective, youth will gain concrete skills, social maturity, discipline, a sense of community responsibility and a cross cultural perspective that comes from personal experience.

The principles taught and lived in the self-governing community will be ones we should hope every person in a democratic society possesses – open-mindedness, critical thinking, fairness, egalitarianism, non-judgmental attitude and a spirit of cooperation. Out of their labor will come the creation of sorely needed infrastructure. Collective members can re-up for as many six-month stints as they desire, through the age of 25, thus creating an even richer long term experience and significant amount of financial gain. Then, from their new perspective, let each American youth begin constructing his or her destiny based on practical, first-hand knowledge gained through cooperative work in a foreign country. Those from developing nations can take a proactive role in their own, their family's and their country's future. We believe an entirely new orientation will emerge from our young people – one that has the communal good in mind and is based on the principles of peace.

One additional page went with it.

URBAN PROJECTS

The Lanes

The idea behind The Lanes is to create a healthy, safe, and fun recreational environment open to the community which also provides employment and training for young adults. The Lanes is a youth operated bowling center housing 10-20 lanes, pool tables, ping-pong tables, a Snack Bar/Cafe and childcare area. The space will be drug and alcohol free. All positions, except for the facility manager, chief mechanic, and some adult supervisors, will be filled by young people ages 18-25. One of the essential rules of The Lanes will be "NO PHYSICAL, VERBAL, EMOTIONAL OR SEXUAL VIOLENCE ALLOWED." It will be a community recreation facility providing supportive instruction and skill building opportunities to enter the world of employment. Collective members will serve in the capacities of front desk reception, Cafe workers, lane maintenance, security, bowling instruction for children, league organizers, childcare workers, and learning technical skills of mechanics and business administration. The Lanes will provide an introduction to the philosophy and operation of the Youth Peace Collective for potential overseas workers, and give returning Collective members a location to share their newly acquired skills and keep connected to the project.

COOPERATION HOUSE

Cooperation House will provide 18-25 year olds with transitional and long-term housing in an affordable, independent, supportive and cooperative setting. The facility will be a hotel, SRO, or apartment type building providing each individual with a room including private bathroom and kitchenette. Members of the Youth Peace Collective will live there for free while they are working with the Collective or in training to go abroad.

Other young adults can stay there if they meet the following requirements: 1) Ability to pay $400/month rent from wages or benefits; 2) Participation in an educational/vocational program or employment; 3) Five hours a week work within Cooperation House;
4) Participation in one service committee; and 5) Attendance at monthly House-wide meetings. The House will be managed by Youth Peace Collective staff operating under a Harm Reduction Philosophy, having the most basic of rules: Respect to Everyone and their Property, No Violent Behavior, No Weapons or Illegal Drugs, No Stealing. The types of tasks that will be included in the resident in-house work component are:
Staffing a 24-hour reception desk, security, maintenance of cleanliness in all common spaces, painting, repairs, etc. On-site counselors will offer individual therapy and workshops in areas such as budgeting, nutrition, stress management, job retention, and conflict resolution. Returning Collective members could use Cooperation House as an option for post-overseas housing.

Chapter 3

I blab to everyone in the world about YPC
and
Oliver and I look for funding

I don't blame my friends if they avoided me back then, because all I did was talk about this great idea I had. Everyone in my field – the circle of folks working with "at-risk" youth – thought it sounded fabulous. Most people said, "When you get it together, seriously, call me. I want to work there." And the kids, forget it, they all wanted to join. The most common responses, after my waxing on about the project were "Sign me up first." "Go to Africa? Fuck, yeah." "Ten thousand dollars? I'm in." When I probed about their ability to follow the no violence part, Mimi, a petite, hard-edged dynamo shrugged her shoulders, " If we can't do it, you'll teach us how, " I asked Thomas, a lanky Afro-American youth who was known for having participated in a fist fight outside Streetwork's Christmas party in the West Village, if he thought he could replace Burger King with African dishes like fufu and fish sauce. He replied, "Well, I'd try."

Finding staff and youth would never be a problem, I thought. There was only one major glitch -- money. Of course we didn't have a penny and funding a brand new project is never easy, particularly in these times of cutbacks and when you need millions, at least. So Oliver and I started on our funding schemes. Oliver, as you can see, is part and parcel of this from the beginning. We knew it was hopeless to try raising money from foundations, after all the proposals I'd written for other projects and the rejection letters I'd gotten. Some unknowns like us had no chance, and we weren't even a 501 (c) (3) non-profit. We needed to find a parent organization.

First we went for the long-shot. I wrote a cover letter and sent our packet to Ted Turner. I had read that he wanted to change the world, thought we'd be better off if women were running things, and was unpredictably independent enough that maybe he'd be interested. I was able to get the name of his personal assistant and sent our materials via what I thought would be the inside track. Never heard a word. Oliver, emphasizing that he was a native of Chicago, sent a packet and letter to Oprah. Maybe we'd get a little something from her Angel Network. No answer. While finishing up the shelter, I wrote Emma Bloomberg, the mayor's daughter. Being young herself, I thought she might see the impact it could have on youth in NYC. We would gladly start a first model project in Manhattan, in fact, I had two buildings picked out a block from the shelter that would be perfect for a huge Cooperation House. Not even an acknowledgment.

By the end of August, 2001 (the legalities of renting the building weren't finalized until February, '01 – six month job, right!) the shelter renovations were perfectly on schedule, a major miracle, you know if you've ever done renovations, and then September 11th happened. Needless to say, things got pushed back a few months. We were hoping to open by Thanksgiving that year, then Christmas, New Years, Valentine's Day. There was a Certificate of Occupancy delay. Our first night was finally 2/22/02 – cosmic, no? A month or so after that I notified Angela that it was time to begin looking for my replacement. I had kept the Youth Peace Collective basically on the back burner for nearly two years, and now I was anxious to start cooking. My successor was found, and I headed on the road to Miami at the end of May, 2002.

The very day I arrived in Miami, John, our construction manager for the shelter renovations in New York, was visiting in Boca Raton. He had been telling me about a friend of his in South Florida who had started his own non-profit, some kind of a school. "Yous have to meet," he said. "He's like you." All three of us met at La Carreta and ate Cuban food. Roy, John's friend, gave me his promotional package for Worldwide Academy, a School for the Adult Learner. I read his materials, liked his idea (a practical, individually oriented, rapid learning method for adults, primarily immigrants, to help them quickly enter the world of employment), visited his sweet little school and discussed whether YPC could start out as a project under their non-profit status. Roy's lawyer and accountant said it could work and I promised him 10% of whatever funds we got. My co-workers at Streetwork had given me $300 as a goodbye present, donation to YPC, and with those funds I bought a fax machine, rented a Post Office Box, and later made copies of the Concept Paper and brochures and put them in spiffy folders. On card stock samples, Jeni designed and printed business cards for Oliver and me. I also gave some money to Roy for a mailing to the "Mini Rich List of Florida" to help Worldwide get some funds, since they were existing on money out of Roy's pocket. Hope that was okay, Streetwork people.

By mid-June Oliver and I were burning up the phone lines trying to formalize our concepts long distance. He was between jobs in Philly and ready for a change, so with the slightest prodding he packed up a rental car, zoomed down I-95 and once he got here we didn't stop writing until we had perfected all our materials. The next part was the hardest – where to look for funding – again.

Somewhere in all of this I was making plans to drive back to New York for the wedding of one of my young cousins. Readers, I must prepare you. Many different cousins are going to appear in these pages and I will try to give each one a descriptive moniker so you can keep them straight. I do ask your forgiveness for having so many cousins who are involved in my life. The groom, my hip-hop anthropologist cousin, was marrying an Argentine woman he had been living with for three years. The wedding on Long Island was going to draw cousins from far off places such as Boulder, Cape Cod, Kansas City and Santa Fe. In the many phone calls to coordinate travel arrangements and who was going to stay where, I spoke to one of my cousins who is a mother of two and a foster mom to many (hereinafter known as foster mom cousin). In the chit-chat of what was going on in our lives, I told her about the Youth Peace Collective, of course. She loved the idea and told me she wished it existed so some of her former foster kids who were turning 18 could join. Then she said a most amazing thing. She told me of a friend she'd known since college who had married a wealthy man and that this friend was extremely generous and, in fact, had wanted her (foster mom cousin) to start a non-profit so the friend could channel money to her to do good things. "Maybe," she proposed, "my friend would be interested in funding your organization." We decided we would talk more at the wedding and I would bring her all our materials. Oliver was going to the wedding too, because he was good friends with hip-hop anthropologist cousin. By the way, the mother of the groom, my cousin who works for a large innovative foundation in Manhattan, had tried months before to present the YPC idea to her boss, but had never been able to get his ear.

The lovely, outdoor wedding was a veritable cousin salad, and many other people were there too. We gave everyone our packets and my Peace Boxes -- hand-painted little treasure boxes with shells from Sanibel Island on the outside and one big shell inside. Each box had "peace" written on it, and the explanation that when you open it up you let peace out into the world. They were my Miami personal funding experiment which I sold at the African Heritage Cultural Arts Center "Village Craft Market." (They were a hit, but I barely made my expenses.) The response to YPC was enthusiastic and encouraging. One wedding guest was going to e-mail us the name of someone in a big San Francisco foundation who was looking for projects for at-risk youth. Foster mom cousin was thrilled with the idea and promised to speak to her friend as soon as possible.

Oliver and I returned to Miami jazzed.

Chapter 4

Patience is a Virtue

Once we got back to Miami I was sure we were going to hear any minute from foster mom cousin, that the response would be positive, and that we'd have to begin moving on details very quickly. Believing that, I went over to see Manny and David, the brothers who own the Tower Hotel, and told them that soon I might be wanting to rent a whole floor. Manny was willing to oversee renovations and teach the youth the basics of construction, and we could turn the Tower into our first Cooperation House. For just $6 million the boys were willing to sell me the 52 room hotel, the house next-door that David and his family lived in, the apartment on the other side where Manny lived with the 4 rental units behind it, and the parking lot. It was a good deal, just one block off Calle Ocho, which is in the midst of a huge rejuvenation. But who had six million? I'd start out renting, and help improve the hotel by adding kitchenettes to the rooms. Each room presently had a private bathroom, and was furnished with a bed, dresser, table, chairs, and a refrigerator. My dream was to buy everything, tear down David's house, and build a three story building for YPC's world headquarters.

A few weeks went by and we didn't hear from foster mom cousin. I hesitated to call, but finally did. She said she had left two messages with her friend's nanny, but had not gotten a call back. She assumed the family was still on summer vacation. "I'll call her right after school starts, and for sure get back to you by mid-September," she told me. Oliver was getting restless. We sent out resumes to all the youth serving agencies in Miami to see if anyone wanted one or the other of us as an employee, with our unique skills. Most did not respond, but Oliver received a call from a Hispanic organization looking for a youth trainer. He set up an interview but cancelled it, deciding that all the good jobs were in New York. He flew up there to see what he could find.

He didn't actually leave for New York until we had heard back from foster mom cousin, in late September. She reported that she had spoken to her friend, but the conversation had taken a direction that afforded her no opportunity to mention our project. In fact, her friend was a bit peeved that she had broken her promise to visit them on the East Coast that fall. Foster mom cousin had recently begun a nursing course, along with her other zillion life activities, and she was so busy that it was impossible to see her friend before February, when the friend and her children would be skiing out West. Foster mom cousin felt the subject of funding the project was best not attempted over the phone, so she consoled me, "You can put it on the back burner [again] if you want, but I'm definitely going to talk to her about it in February. We'll be alone and it will be a good time. Wouldn't it be incredible if she could give you a million dollars to start out?"

That's the number that stuck in my head and the hope I held all through the next long months. I sold peace boxes once a month at the craft fair and went back and forth to my home town, this time helping my mother's older sister, Aunt Mary, who at 85 was rapidly slipping away.

Don't think I lagged though, on setting up my ducks for the Youth Peace Collective. I haven't yet mentioned Tina, my childhood neighbor, but she was in on this from the start, at least in terms of discussing, committing and believing in it. Tina's life was forever changed after her oldest son Aaron died, which she will tell you about later, because it motivated her to want to make YPC a reality. I've designated Tina Director of Operations. All the titles are somewhat superfluous, but she's really good at figuring out practicalities and making things happen. In my vision, every one of the staff was going to be some kind of Director.

Tina was ready to go with us to talk to Antioch College about using their campus for our first summer training. In early May, 2002, driving from the Midwest to NYC, Oliver and I had unexpectedly stopped in on my old alma mater in Ohio, my first time back since graduating in 1972. Have you ever heard of Antioch? It has always been very radical, with its work/study program and activist philosophical orientation. We met with my former philosophy professor, Al Denman, and ran into Irwin Abrams, former history professor, at lunch. Irwin had just published a book about all the Nobel Peace Laureates, which Al ran across the street to buy for Irwin to inscribe. We told them our YPC idea and Al remarked, "Sounds just like an Antiochian." Irwin added, "Maybe you'll be the next ones in my book." Al took us on the grand tour of campus, and when we came to the Antioch Inn (formerly a lovely little hotel, like the kind you would have your parents stay in) and Student Union building, he picked a certain spot downstairs and said, "We've got to start here so you can get the full impact." I was shocked. What I saw was a trashed out pit --- rooms stripped and disheveled, graffiti everywhere, cigarette butts and beer cans strewn around. Al said their census had greatly declined, he never saw the hustle and bustle of students like in my day, and that Antioch's new president would like to see it lean in the direction of a peace university. All the weeks I waited, I kept thinking about the mutually beneficial collaboration YPC could have with Antioch. We needed them and it looked like they needed us. Once we had money, of course.

In those interminable weeks I talked to everyone who had genuinely maintained interest in working with the Collective: Stef in San Francisco, Myriam in Boston but en route to California, Gail, "la hija de" Lucius in NYC, Ernesto in Florida, Stacey, the harm reduction specialist, Mark in K.C., James from the shelter, Anthony, my friend from Ghana now living in London, and Jeni, my graphic designer in Miami. All were on board. "Just let me know when you get the money," they said.

You may feel I'm filling time with this chapter. It's not February yet, so I'm afraid you're having to wait the way we did. Kindly continue, and can you keep hope alive?

Which brings me to another cousin, my ethnomusicologist cousin. He owns the compound that is available for our use in Ghana. The land was given to him by the "Stool Father" – the overseer of the ancestral lands -- of the Volta region near the Togolese border. For years he has taken students from his Texas university in the summer to study African shrine drumming and other ethnomusicology things. His wife offers workshops for people interested in African textiles and tours them through non-commercialized villages where the dyes and materials are made. They have built huts to accommodate 25 students and five staff, which they generally use only for the three summer months. Perfect spot to start a trial collective community, and ethnomusicologist cousin is all for it.

There was a demise during the waiting period. Oliver and I had helped Roy send out over 60 request for proposals to different foundations. A few responded and asked for full proposals, which he sent. He never received one cent, not even from Fannie Mae, and he was teaching Fannie Mae courses. Worldwide Academy was forced to close its doors.

There is a spiritual principle that whenever one door closes, one more opens. That's how it appeared to me when I spoke to Cathy of Storytellers, Inc., a group that works with adjudicated and "at risk" youth in Kansas City. I went to one of their functions, where youth were painting murals, reading poetry, and giving musical and dance performances. The event took place at 39th and Prospect, a dicey, formerly drug dealing corner, for anyone who knows K.C. The banner promoting the event read: "Miracle on 39th Street. Prospect for Change." I know Cathy because her Dad and my Dad go to the same speech therapy group run by Strokes of Support, for stroke survivors. When I explained to her YPC's renewed need for a parent organization, she spoke to Michael, the head of Storytellers, and he determined that our work fell within their mission statement and vision. They were interested, once we had money, of course.

Readers, since we can go no further right now, I believe it is the appropriate moment for me to put something quite personal on the table.

Chapter 5

In which I attempt to establish my credibility as a human being

This whole book is based on your believing me. Since you don't know me, why should you? It is time for me to tell you about myself, and attempt to convince you of my capabilities.

I was born in 1950 in Kansas City, Missouri to a family of two generations of Jewish atheists, on both sides. Jewishness is a cultural and family thing for people like my parents, and it was for my grandparents, who were immigrants from Russia and Poland. One of my great grandfathers had been a religious man, who tried to settle in Palestine in the early 1900's when it was nothing but a malaria infested swamp, so he emigrated to America instead.

I often tell people that I come from a rare entity – a functional family. My parents have been married 56 years and my siblings and I like each other. I have three brothers; I'm the second oldest. When we were growing up we generally got along harmoniously and played creative games with other kids in our neighborhood. Starting when I was 5, we would take summer family car trips all over the U.S. because my father believed his children should see the country they were living in. My father owned a bowling alley when I was a child, and eventually he and his brother went into the building business, like my mother's brothers did. My grandparents, on both sides, were of the leftist/socialist/anarchist bent. They belonged to organizations like the Workman's Circle. Later my father's mother became an ardent Zionist, but that was after some of the famous communists who were World War I conscientious objectors came to my grandparent's farm after they got out of Leavenworth prison and someone causally referred to somebody as "a dirty Jew." Golda Meir used to stay at my grandmother's house when she would come to Kansas City selling Israeli bonds, and in those days she was called Goldie. My mother's first cousin, who lived like a sister in my mother's house from age 12, was the woman who initiated and persisted with the Kansas test case which eventually became the Supreme Court decision of Brown vs. the Board of Education. That woman was hip-hop anthropologist cousin's grandmother, but he never knew her because she died in 1970 of cancer.

All of this is to establish that I come from a family of thinkers and doers. I remember my father teaching us at the dinner table, "Workers of the world unite. You have nothing to lose but your chains." And he explained to me, "Personally, I don't believe in God. I don't believe in Heaven and Hell. What matters is how you treat people here and now." My family was an example of kindness and generosity, and as kids we were given as much freedom as our responsible actions indicated we could handle. We were all excellent students, without ever being told to do our homework.

I went to Antioch College, which I have already mentioned to you. Antioch's work/study plan was perfect for someone like me, who was self-motivated and hungry for life experiences. While on campus, I was always in the library and had jobs as diverse as a teacher's aide in a children's nursery in Rochester, N.Y., building a log cabin near Asheville, N.C., "Girl Friday" for the Lawyer's Constitutional Defense Committee and later the interracial law firm of Elie, Bronstein, Strickler & Dennis in New Orleans, pastry cook in a hotel in Pemaquid Point, Maine, assistant to the Director of LULAC - League of United Latin American Citizens in Corpus Christi, organizer for Prisoners' Reform Project in K.C., and temp for Kodak in Cambridge while I volunteered for the Boston Draft Resistance Group. The most important thing I did during my four years at Antioch was spend one year traveling, by land, alone, from Guatemala to Chile and Argentina. Following Antioch's system, I studied and worked along the way, and received work credits for my weeks of traveling. I lived with a Guatemalan family and studied at the summer school of the University of San Carlos then took Tica Bus all through Central America. In Bogotá I lived with a Colombian family and studied at a Colombian-American Institute Antioch was associated with. Through Ecuador, Peru and Bolivia, I traveled on buses, trains, and hitchhiked on trucks down to Santiago, Chile and arrived there a few days after Allende took office. I spent two months in the southern town of Chonchi, Chiloé, with 100 Chilean youth in a summer volunteer work project where we slept on the floor of a school and helped local carpenters build houses. From there I stopped in Buenos Aires to visit a high school exchange student friend, and then went back to La Paz, Bolivia, where the mother of an Antiochian friend helped me get a job with American Franciscan nuns in a tiny town that had no road, electricity or running water called Apolo. I lived in their convent, taught school in the morning, worked in a medical clinic in the afternoon, and was designated "madrina" of Apollo's soccer team. That year in Latin America changed me. I came away bilingual, multi-cultural, and viewing life from a totally new perspective.

You can see why I hold warmth in my heart for Antioch, and wish to help them any way I can, since I certainly have not been one of their alumni who has contributed to the endowment fund.

After Antioch I proceeded directly to law school. In those days it seemed like attorneys were the ones promoting social change, and that's where I was headed. I went to Rutgers Law School, in Newark, New Jersey and upon graduation received a Reginald Heber Smith Fellowship to work as a legal aid lawyer. I requested a position where I could use my Spanish, and was sent to the Tarrant County Legal Aid Society in Fort Worth, Texas. My salary was $13,000/year.

I'm only going to tell you one story to explain why I quit being a lawyer after one year and will never, never go back. My cases were not criminal, only civil – things like lanlord/tenant disputes, getting people's social security benefits, one school desegregation case (with fantastic plaintiffs, the Mendoza family, where postal worker Rufino and his wife Martina had 10 or so kids in school) and a variety of child custody cases. The case I am about to relate was my first ever appearance in court. It was an interracial child custody case concerning a six year old girl. My clients were the black father and his mother, who had been the child's caretaker since birth. The child's mother was a crazed white lady who happened, somehow, to be a lawyer. The mother had never shown any interest in the child, but was suddenly in court to get custody away from the father, who had entrusted the daughter's care to his mother. Grandmother and granddaughter were very close and loving with one another. In the Judge's chambers, my buddy Judge W.(I am respectfully not using his name), who used to always invite me into chambers for a cup of coffee since there were only 8 female attorneys in Ft. Worth at that time and we were something of a novelty, spoke to me frankly. "Janet, you aren't going to win this case because your client is a drug addict." My client had been busted for taking valium across state lines. "And furthermore," he added self-righteously, "I'm not going to let a little white girl live in a black neighborhood." The granddaughter looked racially mixed, but more white than black. No surprise; I lost the case. After the decision came down the mother grabbed the little girl in her arms and tried to carry her out of the courtroom. The girl screamed, cried and pounded on her mother, finally jumping out of her arms and running over to me imploring through tears, "Janet, tell Judge W. I don't want to go with my mother. Tell Judge W." So I stomped back into chambers, knocking first, to relate to the Judge what was occurring. In his smug Texas drawl he advised me, "Don't let it bother you, Janet." That was the moment I told myself, I'll finish my year's contract and leave this profession so I will never again have to call anyone Your Honor, and thankfully, to this day, I haven't. My final comment here is: I never saw a legal case resolve any real, human situation; it just puts people farther apart. If the parties don't want to do what the court orders them to, they find a way to get around it somehow or keep on appealing. If anything, mediation is the forum we should promote for solving people's conflicts – nobody wins, nobody loses, both sides have to compromise.

Much to the chagrin of my parents, who loved saying "my daughter, the lawyer," after I left the legal profession I traveled to many cities in the United States and various countries, doing a number of different jobs including: temporary secretary, motel maid, waitress, grapefruit picker, cow milker, t-shirt seller, prep cook, laundry attendant, dishwasher, cookie batter maker, and bagel salesperson. The entire year of 1987 was spent traveling by land through 15 African countries and teaching English for three months in Yaoundé, Cameroon. For 8 months in 1990 I taught English in Buenos Aires, Argentina. Often the work I've done has been as a volunteer, such as two humanitarian caravans to Cuba with IFCO/Pastors for Peace, as a fundraiser/resource developer for two street youth projects in Durban and Johannesburg, South Africa, for Integración Juvenil, a program for disadvantaged youth in Puerto Plata, Dominican Republic and for Casa Rosada, an orphanage for children with AIDS in Santo Domingo. In 1996 I developed Enfants a L'ecole, a small orgnization that existed for two years paying school fees for underprivileged children in Haiti.

My first entrance into the world of "homeless" youth came in the early 80's when I went cold turkey (as I went to every city, on the Greyhound bus, not knowing anybody and having to find a place to live in one day and a job within a week) to St. Pete, Florida.

I worked at Plantation House, a shelter for children taken from their homes because of child abuse allegations. After six months there, I was hooked – on teenagers. That group of kids who drive people insane; I loved working with them. Their honesty, resilience, unpredictability, and vibrant struggle for life captivated me.

When I went cold turkey to San Francisco in 1984, I kept a watch out for jobs working with the same population. I became a counselor at the recently opened Diamond Street Youth Shelter, paid by VISTA ($400/month and told we could not have a second job), run by Catholic Charities, providing San Francisco's only open door nightly shelter for run-away youth. That shelter was run as a collective. Suffice it to say, the shelter became my life and in a year, when the first director stepped down, I was given the job. During my short reign of one year, we bought a building (the shelter had started in the basement of a church off Castro street, where we had to entirely dismantle our furnishings every Sunday morning before 9 a.m. so the parishioners could play bingo), renovated it, dropped the "Street" in our name, expanded staff, secured real salaries, and wrote enough grants to get funding for a couple years. As much as I loved the shelter, I hated that my job mainly consisted of crawling on my knees and begging for money. I quit the directorship and returned to being an overnight counselor, just before I left for my year in Africa.

When I returned from Africa I went back to San Pancho, as the Mexican youth called S.F., and worked for Innovative Housing. I started a cooperative living house in the Mission District exclusively for youth, and I was live-in staff. Oy vey. From the five original residents, we usually never had less than nine or ten kids living there, and they would leave dirty dishes in their rooms until the pizza had petrified and the glasses were encrusted for life. After six months as a house parent, I left politically correct California for Costa Rica.

Armed with a tiny piece of paper from the Tico Times – Costa Rica's English language newspaper – with a classified looking for donations for a street youth project, I set out to find Kukula. I found them, a program run at that point by a former Peace Corps volunteer, and worked six months in Limon, on the Atlantic coast, setting up their newly created "Repostería" (bakery). We made banana bread, carrot cake and chocolate chip cookies that we sold in the Saturday market. Two years later I returned to Kukula to be house manager for their new location and help bring their programs for youth to the marginal neighborhoods of that overlooked port town. When I returned from my first Costa Rican trip, I worked as an overnight counselor in Miami's homeless youth shelter, the Miami Bridge.

It was after I returned from my second stint in Costa Rica that I got the first job at Streetwork. As I've said before, Oliver and I were outreach partners, along with Ines and Warren, may he rest in peace. This meant that four nights a week we spent from 8 p.m. to 11 p.m. walking the parts of town where kids hung out or prostituted and handed out lunches, condoms, and other safe sex materials. Each day we worked, we counseled individual clients for 5 or 6 hours before going on outreach. Streetwork's drop-in center is located in the middle of Times Square, and I feel safe in saying they work with the most disenfranchised kids in the City.

By way of ending this chapter, I wish to say: For the past twenty years I have worked with kids who murder and kids who have been murdered. Young people who have been sexually assaulted by fathers, mothers, brothers, aunts, uncles, grandfathers, brothers' friends, neighbors, mother's boyfriends, mental hospital staff, group home counselors, teachers, school security guards, bosses, priests, and foster parents. Youth who have been emotionally and physically abused by the same, or expanded, list above. Gay, lesbian, bisexual, transgender and transsexual youth who have been beaten up. Kids who had hot sauce poured down their throats. Were chained to beds and radiators and locked in dark closets. Kids who pimped and were pimped. Kids who couldn't take it any more and killed themselves. Kids addicted to coke, crack, heroin and speed. Kids forced to eat their food out of dog bowls on the floor. Kids left in cars, empty houses, hotels, and on street corners.

Maybe I haven't heard it all, but I've heard a lot. And you know what stands out the most in my mind? The unquenchable will to love and be loved of all these children of a mother and father somewhere though they never got parented right. No, not at all. Yet the youth want to go on and do something and be somebody, and I want to give them that chance. Not a band-aid. Not a servile, minimum wage, go nowhere job. I want to give them a place where they are treated fairly and respectfully, are expected and encouraged to work hard and learn as much as they can, and then to pay them wonderfully well. Show me a kid who would go into the military and train to kill people or possibly be killed, rather than create something positive on earth, and be paid equally, if not better, for it.

I rest my case.

Chapter 6

The phone call we've been waiting for
and
The Chapter which establishes this as a work of fiction

It was about seven o'clock one evening and I was preparing my famous soup – enhanced top ramen. I was initially introduced to ramen (which you can buy, at worst 3 for $1 and at best 10 for $1 – can't beat that) on a large scale when I lived with the youth in San Francisco. It was their main cooked staple. My version is expanded and more nutritional. Here's the procedure: Put in a saucepan any vegetables you want in your soup, suggestions are broccoli, zucchini, definitely onions and garlic, cabbage, carrots, green beans, whatever. Then add small cut chunks of tofu, or I guess if you hate tofu you can leave it out, but it's part of the healthiness. Cover the veggies with water and boil, adding any spices you like. On the side in a bowl place one heaping tablespoon of miso. Do you know miso? It's from soy beans and it comes in a paste. There are various varieties of miso, each with a different taste, but my favorites are red miso and brown rice miso. Crush up the ramen in the closed package and then open it and throw out that flavor packet – it's full of chemicals. When the veggies boil, pour some of their water into your miso bowl (miso itself should not boil) and mush up the miso in the water so there are no lumps, while at the same time you've thrown the noodles into the soup and are intermittently stirring them for their prolonged cooking time of three minutes. After noodles are done, turn off stove, pour dissolved miso in, stir, and let it steep for a few minutes. Violá.

A wonderfully nourishing meal in less than 10 minutes – if you have it down the way I do.

Anyway, I was in the midst of my soup, somewhere like the throw in the noodles stage, when the phone rang. My stomach gave a jump, and I didn't know why. Thank goodness for cordless phones, because I picked it up and said hello while I continued to mush and stir intermittently. It was foster mom cousin. "Hi," she said. "Are you sitting down?" "No, I'm standing up." "Well, sit down," she laughed, already a good sign. "I can't," I explained, "I'm in the middle of cooking soup." She told me anyway. "She said YES! She loves your idea and wants to send you a check right away, after she talks to her accountant. She's giving you one million. Who should she send it to?"

"No way," I said, stunned, still stirring. "Really?" "Of course really," foster mom said. "Really? That's fabulous. That's wonderful. I can't believe it. Really, really?" "YES!" she practically yelled. Then I started in on my thank you, thank you, thank you, this could never have happened without you and I can't believe you have helped me this way and that you and your friend will have blessings on your children and your children's children for all eternity because you're helping bring peace to the earth, and all kinds of things like that. Then my soup boiled over the stove top.

Well, there it was. The green light. Full speed ahead.

Chapter 7

Sprint Makes Money on Me

We talked a while longer but finally I think she got tired of hearing me say thank you so much, so she said she had to go because her youngest foster child was crying.

Bad timing! It was only 7:30 p.m. and my Sprint PCS unlimited minutes didn't start until 9:00 p.m. (it was a weekday). I had only two days left in my month's payment cycle and only 7 minutes left in any-time minutes. If I went over, I'd be charged at 40 cents a minute, you know. So I made some calls on my Working Assets long distance, but I knew what was going to happen. Lots of call-backs started coming in on my cell phone, because my home phone was tied up and it was a local call for the New York people.

Do you even have to wonder who my first call was? Oliver, of course. Then Tina, Stef, Stacey, Ern, and on down the line. Everyone was jubilant. When I told Oliver, the first words out of his mouth were "No way! Really?" (I'm not kidding.) I told everybody I needed to make some calls and arrangements and get the legal status and finances worked out, and then I would get back to them with the date of the first staff meeting. I intended to fly everybody to Miami for a week and house them at the Tower Hotel. We'd have meetings in my apartment and I'd get some kind of vouchers made for El Pub and Exquisito, so folks could eat out here in the hood.

Here's how my conversation with my mother went. Me: Mom, guess what? Her: What? Me: We got a million dollars! Her: You're kidding. Me: No. Oh, hold on a second, my cell phone is ringing. Hello – James, call you right back, I'm on the other line. Are you at home? (me to myself, another cell minute gone) Mom, are you there? Her: Yes. Me: So what do you think? Her: Great. Me: That's all you think? Just great. Her: Well, that's wonderful. Did you really get the money? Me: Yes! Her: I can't believe it. Me: Well, we did. Her: Are you sure? Me: I'm sure. Okay, gotta go, mom. Tell Dad. I'll talk to you tomorrow. Her: Okay, bye doll.

Three more cell calls came in. Even if I don't answer them I use up minutes listening to the voice mail messages. Doesn't that seem a bit unfair? Gail, Myriam, Mark. I had to talk to them all. Couldn't possibly call Anthony in London. Jeni, thankfully, was local. I was cutting it close to the wire. Oh, I couldn't forget Al Denman; he would be ecstatic. Gotta run over and let Manny and David know.

Cathy in Kansas City was my longest call. She said she would give Michael the good news immediately and we mapped out a game plan for the initial bases we needed to cover. I'd be there in a couple of weeks and we'd meet with a lawyer, accountant, and work on some proposals for matching grants. This was a godsend for Storytellers too, because, as a small, grassroots project, they have always struggled for funding.

An unexpected cell call from a friend I've known since Junior High. "Oh Chaiky, can't talk right now, but guess what? The Youth Peace Collective just got funded!" "Yippeee," she hollered, "Call me later."

Oliver had a quick few questions – he's in New York so he called on the cell. Tell me it ain't so. I think I went over a minute.

Sprint, I have another bone to pick with you. Your headquarters are in Overland Park, Kansas (or Prairie Village, Shawnee Mission, Leawood, whatever you want to call it) and all over the Kansas City area my phone is constantly going "out of service area." What's up with that? My friend Mary, who runs a company called Party Personnel, was once calling your service department to complain about losing calls and she was right next to Sprint Campus (that's what they call their mass of buildings) and the call dropped. Hey guys, I know you're trying hard and I super appreciate the convenience of your phone service, but could you beef up the satellite dishes in K.C.?

And you only made 40 cents off me, on what is maybe the happiest day of my life, thus far.

Chapter 8

The First Staff Meeting

Collaborating with Storytellers was a breeze. We worked together efficiently, logically, and things were set up for YPC to start out under their auspices, retaining the autonomy to run in exactly its own style, with the understanding that in probably two or three years we would become our own 501 (c) (3). Cathy and I churned out four grant proposals to large foundations known to care about youth issues, and we asked each one to match the million dollars. Hey, we told them, we're starting the most innovative project around and you'd be lucky to hop on the boat now (we used "grantese" language to say it), but you can only do that once you have some money in hand.

The million dollar check was written to Storytellers, Inc. As we had agreed and is common for parent organizations, Storytellers received 10% and the rest went into a Youth Peace Collective account, on which Michael and I were the authorized signatories. I knew Michael, an artist, would be wonderful to work with when I saw him in action at that event I visited on 39th and Prospect. Two teenaged girls were giving their performance, a rap song with some dance steps. The girls weren't too coordinated in their dancing style, and I didn't really pay attention to the words of the song, but all of the sudden Michael walked up to them and said firmly but gently, "Stop." The girls stopped midstep. He spoke to them. "Remember we said all performances had to be of a positive nature, with no negative language? I don't think yours fits this category.

I'm sorry." The girls looked a little embarrassed, giggled and then walked off stage – not mad. Now that's a skill – to tell a kid in the middle of a public performance that what they're doing isn't right, and to not make them feel bad. Yes, I wanted to work with that man. And Cathy, she's a woman after my own heart. We realized that when we knew both of us had spent time in Ouagadougou (bet you don't even know where it is).We gab non-stop outside of speech class every time we both bring our fathers.

Once I knew the money was available, I began calling everyone to pick a mutually convenient week to meet -- no easy task with 10-15 different busy lives. We agreed on the second week of March. I told everybody to make their own plane reservations and I would reimburse them at the meeting. Rooms were reserved at the Tower and I set up accounts at various local restaurants where I prepaid a certain amount, and each meal the staff ate, plus a 20% tip, would be discounted. There were three of us in town with cars, so I figured we could shuttle to and from the airport, which is only 15 minutes from my apartment and the Tower, to pick everybody up.

I guess now is the moment. Drum roll please. I want to introduce to you the initial staff of the Youth Peace Collective.

Director of Development – me.

Director of Training – Oliver. Don't you feel like you already know him? Besides Streetwork, he has worked at youth serving agencies in New York, San

Francisco and Philadelphia. Out on his own at age 16, he has lived experiences similar to many youth he works with. As a counselor he is warm, sensitive, insightful, and possesses dynamic ability as a trainer. Everything he does exudes creativity. I've never met anyone with a more incredible knowledge and love of music – frequently he compiles tapes and introduces me to fascinating musicians. I trust Oliver explicitly and know he sees situations with a sharp and discerning eye.

Director of Operations – Tina. I've known her since she was three years old. For years she worked in sales and raised two children, but after Aaron died, she switched careers and became a Tour Guide. She organizes, coordinates, researches, and has the ability to visualize a situation and make it work out. All her life she lived in Kansas City, but has recently moved to the Seattle area. In the last few years she has been devouring books on spirituality and is quite convinced that the world is on the verge of a major shift of consciousness.

Director of Community Relations– Gail. Gail is a lifelong activist. I met Gail on the first Pastors for Peace Cuba "Friendshipment" caravan in 1992; she was one of the organizers. She worked at IFCO (Interreligious Foundation for Community Organization) for many years and got her Master's in Media Studies. Everyone loves Gail. She has an engaging sense of humor and unshakeable commitment to equality. She's been to hundreds of demonstrations, surely thousands of political meetings, and is always a respected voice of reason and thoughtfulness.

Director of Procurement and Logistics – Ernesto. Born in Barranquilla, Colombia, Ernie lived in Miami from age 12. I met him 25 years ago. He's married to my "soul sister," Myra, a Cuban-American professor of multi-ethnic literature. Ernie's the one who will find out where we can get massive quantities of irrigation tubing, or what's the best way to transport it to Africa. He worked in the import/export business for many years and will absolutely know how to find anything we need. He also gives creative, appropriate nicknames to most everyone, which is often helpful for comic relief.

Director of Personnel – Stef. Stef was the Clinical Coordinator of Diamond Youth Shelter when I was the Director, and she was a rock of Gibraltar for us all. She has a Masters in Marriage, Family and Child Counseling. There is no one better than Stef to have by your side in the middle of a crisis or difficult situation – she speaks and acts with knowledge, wisdom and straightforwardness. Formerly she ran an independent living program in San Francisco and has a private therapy practice. She's raised four children, and loves horses.

Director of Communications – Myriam. I met Myriam when she was Manhattan foundation cousin's roommate. She grew up outside Boston, of Haitian parents. Over the years she's worked in politics, the music business, catering, as a waitress, on theater projects, and as public relations coordinator for a "high risk" youth program. She's spunky, irreverant, and loves to travel. I just wish she wouldn't come through

Miami airport on a layover at 5:30 a.m. and call me up to take her for a Cuban coffee.

Director of Work Crews – Mark. Aaron's father is Mark; he's Tina's ex-husband. His life story out-matches any youth I've ever worked with, a white kid growing up in Watts in L.A. He's seen it all, done it all, and is trying to live to tell the story. For years Mark practically ran a youth shelter in his own home, taking in his children's friends or other youth in need. He's been a laborer, installing flooring for much of his working life. He has a voice that you can hear across a ball field, especially when he's encouraging his son, the pitcher.

Director of Harm Reduction and Healing – Stacey. A native New Yorker, Stacey was a collective member of Diamond, and then returned to her hometown to work 14 years at Streetwork. It was because of Stacey I initially got the job there. She started a Lower East Side youth drop-in program out of the Needle Exchange, and later developed a separate Streetwork site for that very unique population of kids. She's been a trainer and practitioner of harm reduction for years, and presented at conferences all over the world.
Stacey also sings in a girl band that tours Eastern Europe.

Director of Orientation – James I hired James as an overnight staff for the Streetwork shelter and promoted him to Shelter Manager. He grew up in the projects in Brooklyn and spent many years paying a debt to society, as a result of some of his actions. James was my right hand at the shelter; a man with a passion for his job. He's about to receive his Associate's Degree in Social Services, the first person in his family to go to college. On James' third interview for the Shelter job, he tried to help break up a fight at Streetwork Drop-in and was practically choked.

Well, that's ten of us for full-time staff. But there are a few other people I've invited to the first staff meeting. I can't get Anthony here – too far away and he's in the midst of his medical studies and practice, though he will surely join us before we start in Ghana. I also want to bring Florence over. She's my Cameroonian friend who nursed me to health when I had malaria, and I know she'd be perfect to work in the administrative area. Getting visas for her and others, like Thabisile and Tate in South Africa, will take some time, and is therefore the subject of another chapter.

Cathy, of course, is coming as a representative of Storytellers. Jeni, who's already in town, will participate in the meetings that pertain to her because she's helping us with our promotional materials. Jeffrey will be formulating our budgets and overseeing the finances, on an hourly basis. He's Stacey's cousin, doing freelance work for non-profits. Adrian, a Costa Rican friend who lost his job in the financial district after 9/11, will be setting up our computer systems. And the cherry on top of the sundae: Deb, Amma Mama. My friend Deb from San Francisco is a practitioner of "Amma," a Japanese form of massage. Deb will give massages (she'll only be able to bring her chair, not her table) to any staff who want or need it. I plan to have Deb come to summer training and possibly travel to different cities to offer her skills to all

Collective members. Some of the above mentioned folks will be working as consultants, on an as-need basis, shall we say.

Get this! At approximately 9 a.m. Monday morning as people filed into my apartment, after walking over from the Tower (everyone arrived on Sunday), almost every single person made a comment to indicate they weren't really pleased with their title designations. What an example of consensus decision-making. In one minute they unanimously threw out their job titles and decided they all wanted to be called "Coordinator." Jeepers, I kind of liked being Director of Development.

In reality, my apartment was too small to fit us comfortably. There were 15 bodies present. We made do though, with blankets and pillows I brought out to sit on, plus some beach chairs from the trunk of my car. We spent the first day discussing essentials about the direction we wanted to initially go. At no point will I belabor you with details of conversations, or how decisions were reached collectively, just know it's time consuming, sometimes patience-trying and not infrequently repetitive. Everyone gets their say; no opinion is squelched. When it's over, each person feels that his or her point of view has been laid on the table, and though the final decision may not be the one you preferred, you agree to abide by it. That's the basic principle of collectivity. Not that we actually had disagreements about issues. It was more a matter of different ideas on the most effective ways of going about certain things.

We decided the following: 1) In the first year it was impossible for us to pull together the Africa component; our energies were better focused on establishing model urban projects and solidifying our training methodology. 2) Kansas City made sense as the first location, because Storytellers was there and real estate was fairly cheap. 3) The theoretical headquarters could be Miami, but they were just doing that to make me happy. 4) Different groupings of staff would work in the regions (the group divided up the U.S.in a fashion that felt logical and equitable) and together devise their strategy for seeking, informing, interviewing, and selecting candidates. 5) Our first training would happen this summer, provided Antioch agreed. It was already March so that meant "poner las pilas" (put the batteries in) and get to work. 6) The first training would be a full three months long, emulating the community operations format of four days of work and one day of training. 7) We needed to meet again around the end of April to check-in with one another and see how things were going.

I should mention that the first morning we were all together, everyone went around and told their stories, however they wanted to tell them, by way of general introduction. Of course, various of the individuals already knew one another. Stacey had worked with James and Oliver at Streetwork, Stef at Diamond, and knew Jeffrey all her life. Ernie had met Stef and James when they visited me in Miami, and Jeni had often been at his house. Tina was buddies with Oliver, had met James in NYC, and, you recall, been married to Mark. Myriam knew Oliver. Oliver knew Jeffrey,

James, Jeni and Ernie. Amma Mama knew Ernie and Stef. Cathy, Adrian and Gail only knew me.

Everyone got along smoothly. A few vignettes will give you an idea of the group dynamic. After one particularly arduous day of hammering out our mission statement, outlining the Collective Agreement that youth would have to sign before entering summer training, and presenting our visions for where we wanted YPC to be in five years, the group decided they wanted to go to the beach. We had three cars: Ernie's, Jeni's and mine; there were 15 of us – workable. I suggested a spot on North Beach, easy to get to, uncrowded, free parking lot. Ernie hates Miami Beach and wanted to go to Cape Florida on the end of Key Biscayne – a toll bridge and paid parking away, but in his opinion, a more appealing beach. Seven people wanted to go with Ernie; eight with me. Not workable. Ernie and I extolled the virtues of our respective beaches, and one person jumped ship to my side, not that I had any proprietary interest. We were still at loggerheads. Stef asked all the people who were interested in Cape Florida if they were diehards in their decision. Three said they were not. She wrote down on one slip of paper "North Beach," and on two "Cape Florida." They were placed in a bowl, and the three picked. Thus we ended up with two cars to North Beach and Ernie's one. All of this happened in about 10 minutes, and we were off to get some Florida sun.

Amma Mama was a popular figure at that first staff meeting. When anybody got stressed out or feeling tired or achy they would ask for a 15 minute chair massage, which Deb set up in my bedroom. Deb's technique was to sit you down, ask if you had any particularly sore spots or injuries that she should know about, and then inquire if you could spell ukulele (could you spell it if I hadn't written it for you? I couldn't; I had to look it up in the dictionary.). Then she would give this most wonderful, sensitive, through your clothing, relaxing massage. Everybody walked out of that room with what Deb calls, "the buddha smile." Some got a little too relaxed, like when Mark fell asleep after his massage and started snoring. Tina gave him the elbow. Gail came out of the bedroom saying, "Girl, you've got magic hands." At the end of the week the group gave Amma Mama a fancy looking certificate that Jeni created which said:

TO AMMA MAMA
for

THE BEST MASSAGE
and
THE WORST JOKES

(When do we get the table?)

Love,
(everybody signed their names)

It's true. Deb is an arsenal of bad jokes, but she gives a killer massage.

The final scenario is short and sweet. The last afternoon of the last day, I asked everyone to say how they were feeling about the process we had just gone through, the work we were proposing to do, and the experience of being in the collective. Myriam wanted to start, and she said: "I've never felt so close, so quickly to a group of people. I'm honored to be in the midst of such talent, compassion and vision. What we're doing is incredible. I believe in it completely and think we're about to change the world. Thank you, you guys." And she got up and gave me a hug. Then she went around the room giving everyone else a hug. Somehow, beginning in silence but bursting into laughter, eveybody began to hug everyone else. It wasn't mushy, more like a dance, in which we changed partners at every beat. Then Mark said, "I think we're the bomb!"

The way things were left was: Oliver, Gail, Stacey and James would work the Northeast Region; Myriam, Stef and Tina the Northwest and Southwest; Mark, Cathy and I getting things together in Kansas City (Midwest Region); and Ernie, Jeni, Adrian, Jeffrey (though he would operate from NYC) and me as part of the headquarters and Southeast Region. Myriam and I would design an Application form that we'd e-mail to everyone for comments and changes, and each region would contact programs working with "at risk" youth to start informing potential candidates. We felt the appropriate number of youth for the first training session was 100, coming somewhat evenly from each of the regions. We were waiting to hear about other grants before deciding on full-time salaries, so all of us were on hourly wage, for about a month. Tina would find a reasonably priced and good coverage benefit package. Stef would draft a Policy and Procedures Manual. Adrian would be designing a computer program that would ultimately be installed on everyone's computers, because most people would be working from home. Jeni was creating brochures, stationery, and business cards to be ready in two weeks, and t-shirts that we wanted to have by the summer. Oliver and Stacey were going to plan a "train the trainer" session for staff that would be presented at our April meeting. I needed to call Antioch, and, assuming they were interested, plan a meeting that any of the ten of us who could, would attend.

Friday afternoon I told them they had the whole weekend free – wasn't that big of me?

Chapter 9

Youth Peace Collective's Position on War

War is the business of killing. If you agree with the premise that it is acceptable for a government to commit murder and homicide for whatever reasons they choose to give, you have blood on your hands. The existence of war encourages violence as a means of resolving disagreements within a society. War places individuals who have not been decision makers in the position of losing their lives, or taking another's, to further the political, economic, territorial, or religious goals of their "leaders." War is destructive, irrational and cruel.

The Golden Rule must guide all of our actions. Killing in retribution does not reverse a death or stop the cycle of violence. As human beings we must rise to our highest potential, which is inherently constructive and life-affirming. We, ourselves, must be examples of living cooperatively, showing fairness and respect to all. Only by taking responsibility for our individual actions, can we begin to repair the damage inflicted over thousands of years by humans attempting to dominate one another.

Chapter 10

The Application

YOUTH PEACE COLLECTIVE APPLICATION

Note: You may answer in writing (with someone helping, if needed) or by audiotape.

Name ______________ **Date of Application** _______
Date of Birth _______ **Place of Birth** ____________
Best Address to Reach You ___________________
Best Phone Number and/or E-mail to Reach You ___________________________
How did you hear about the Youth Peace Collective? ____
Describe yourself in one word ___________________
Who is the person you most respect in your life and why? ____
____
____
____
If you were the most influential person in the world, what would you do to bring about peace?
____
____
____
____
____
____

What is the best thing you feel you have done in your life? ______________________________

____

____

What is the worst thing you feel you have done in your life? ______________________________

____

____

What qualities in others bother you the most?

____

____

____

How would your friends describe you? __________

____

____

What are the most important activities in your life right now? ______________________________

____

____

What do you want to do during your life? ________

____

____

What do you fear? ____________________________

____

What always makes you smile? ________________

____

What would you do with $10,000? ______________

____

Why do you want to join the Youth Peace Collective? ______________________________

____

____

How would you answer these questions?

Chapter 11

A Quickie Trip to K.C.

The Kansas City crew had their plate full. They needed to find sites for The Lanes and Cooperation House because youth joining the Collective after summer training were going to start their work in my beloved hometown. For this, I had two aces up my sleeve.

Do you recall my telling you that my mother's brothers were builders? In Jewish families that means when my uncles retired, my cousins took over the business. These "apartment cousins" currently owned and operated a huge number of rental units throughout the K.C. area, in Missouri and Kansas. Apartment cousins had one medium sized complex near 39th and Rainbow Avenue, just two blocks from State Line, on the Kansas Side. All the units were studios. I had lived there once for six months while I was working as a translator and assistant for an immigration lawyer friend of mine. Rentals had been down, I mean way down, in the past year, so apartment cousins were amenable to the idea of YPC renting the entire complex at reduced rates. It would ensure full occupancy and we would take over management of the place. Some staff members would also live on site. YPC would offer present occupants a bonus for breaking their leases, and we would try to have as many units as possible available by September. The rest of the apartments we would take over as the tenants' leases came up, and in the meantime some youth might have to share a studio. That wouldn't be so bad, because they were good-sized.

The second ace had to do with my dear old (88 years) dad. Northeast Bowl. As a child, every Sunday after our alternative, non-religious Jewish Cooperative Sunday School, my dad would take us to the bowling alley he owned. We loved going there. I remember sitting behind the lanes with the pin spotters; that was before automatic pin setters came in. His place had 8 lanes, a few pool tables and pin-ball machines and a little luncheonette (maybe it was a bar, too). I learned to bowl at age four or five, first with two hands, and later on joined leagues, which were quite the rage in the 50's.

On a Saturday Dad and I took graphic designer cousin (yes, another one) on a field trip to the northeast section of town. We drove past 9th and Benton where Dad as a first grader in 1922 sat on a curb watching General Pershing in a parade celebrating the World War I victory. We went past his Uncle Ben's hardware store on E. 9th, Dr. Dicky's who "had wanted to adopt pop (his father)," Lyon's Grocery store where the groceries were delivered by cart and a horse with the same name as his brother, the two brick houses his pop had built on 10th and Kensington, to Elmwood and St. Johns Avenue, where the bowling alley was located. It was now called Sal & Jerry's Northeast Bowl and was closed. It would feel like a karmic coup if I could get that place.

That Monday, at the Strokes of Support speech class, I told Cathy about the excursion. She assured me she could find out who owned the building and if it was for sale. When we told our dads what we were scheming, mine said, "I hope you get it for the same price I did in 1947," in that slowly enunciated post-stroke way he speaks. Cathy's dad quipped, "When do I get to bowl?" Both our fathers provide us with quite a bit of humor since their strokes. After Cathy's father spent weeks in the hospital, partly in a coma with his first stroke, she returned from out of the country and greeted him "Hi Dad, I've just come from Africa." He responded, "Me too, and I want to go back."

Cathy and Mark were going to be more than busy with the groundwork for the two projects. I wished I could have stayed longer, but because of other meetings, I had only four days in Kansas City, barely enough time to grab some caffeine and chat with my friends, the owners of Muddy's Coffeehouse, or see my Aunt Mollie, whose 90 year old husband is the horse's namesake.

Chapter 12

We all go to Antioch

All the Coordinators, plus Amma Mama, worked out their schedules to make that first trip to Antioch. As expected, Al Denman had been thrilled when I told him our great news and he had quickly arranged for us to meet Antioch's president and present our project. In a series of meetings with members of the administration and faculty, they agreed that we could have use of 125 dorm rooms, pay the cafeteria cooks to stay on during the summer (YPC youth would be prep cooks, dish washers, servers etc.), hire three Antioch students part-time as liaisons and coordinators in our absence, and that we would not be charged for use of the campus because our "labor of peace" would be considered a barter. We were going to renovate the Antioch Inn and Student Union. There was even some discussion of allowing youth who had successfully completed stints at YPC to have special dispensation to become Antioch students, but that would be worked on later. Also, maybe Antioch students could work with YPC as a co-op job.

We spent three days there, looking over every part of the campus. After the Inn and the Union, in subsequent summers, North Hall dorm could use our help. Folks took walks in Glen Helen, the beautiful forest that is adjacent to campus. Ate at Ya Ya's pizzeria in "downtown" Yellow Springs. Soaked in the long standing vibes of unconventional students who have graced these hallowed grounds, where the college's first president, Horace Mann, uttered the words " Be ashamed to die until you have won some victory for humanity." That's what we were trying to do, win a victory for ol' humanity.

We decided the first week of training would be a combination of beginning workshops on collective living, and a lot of practical construction education. Mark would draw up a plan for work groups, but was leaning towards have 10 youth per group with an adult supervisor. He and the Antioch students would be looking for a local architect and construction company that could design and oversee the renovations, and for carpenters who were willing to become trainers for the youth. Various staff mentioned carpenters who would love spending the summer helping us get going, Tauno for one, from Streetwork and Dean in Albuquerque who had worked with Pastors for Peace. Mark and Ernie stayed on a week after the rest of us left and took charge of hiring the students and getting the ball rolling on everything else.

There was one extremely heated discussion during our visit. I was adamant about there being no television on campus during training. I have quite strong opinions about that medium (to say the least, and which you are about to read) and some agreed, but others felt I was being absurd and unyielding. After over an hour of spirited back and forth, with blood pressures rising and nothing resolved, Amma Mama jumped into the conversation, "Did you hear what happened to the frog that parked in the red zone?" Us: "No." Deb: "Toad" (get it, towed). We cracked up. Tension released; discussion tabled.

Chapter 13

My Sermon Against Television
Sorry Readers, I Must

Dear Brothers and Sisters, I am worried about you. Instead of living your own unique, firsthand experiences 24 hours each day, as our ancestors did for eons, you are watching television. Your eyes are focusing on a multitude of little lights projecting images and ideas into your brains, which you then digest and believe to be real. Television is controlled by a small number of large and wealthy corporations, who have many selfish motives for deciding what to present in that forum which they dominate. You are their captive audience.

It's always shocking to me to return to the United States after spending time out of the country and realize how much Americans' conversation is about things they see on TV. People tell you plots of sitcoms and funny scenes, relating with glee and enthusiasm accounts of what imaginary characters have said and done. Or they talk about a drama involving police, hospitals, investigators, mafiosos, whatever, and claim it's so realistic, when they most likely would not know because they have never lived those realities. Let's not even mention the "news" which purports to be fact, but is given in a tone of voice and graphic style that exudes fabrication. Everyone is sitting and staring at pundits talking, people baring their souls, crazy competitions for money, shopping, everybody interviewing everybody else, music acted out, sports, soap operas, cameras following situations pretending to be natural, the weather, old movies, new movies, nature, documentaries, games, award presentations, and whatever else I forgot to mention. Oh, commercials is what I forgot.

I have not had a television since I left home for college at 17. So how do I know about all the above-mentioned programming? Because people tell me, of course. And need I say that everywhere I go I encounter the box: in restaurants, corner stores, car repair waiting rooms, the laundromat, bars, the airport. Nearly every American household I walk into has a TV on. It is, in my opinion, the most severe, pernicious addiction our society has.

My bible is the book *Four Arguments for the Elimination of Television*, written in the late 70's by Jerry Mander, a former public relations and advertising executive. I call it my bible because whenever I'm feeling down, I open up any page, read selections, and it brings me solace. The book's first passage sends chills up my spine. Mr. Mander refers to humans' progressive movement into entirely artificial environments (man-made, as opposed to natural), causing a break in our direct knowledge of and contact with the planet. This state of disconnection, he says, creates the inability to distinguish truth from fiction, thus setting up appropriate conditions for the implantation of arbitrary realities. Television, through its technological ease and widespread acceptance, accelerates this problem. What music to my soul! Mr. Mander encourages people to understand that the primal reason for television's existence, irrespective of programming, is to sell products. As someone formerly ensconced in the image-making field, he offers the simple truth that advertising only exists to convince people to buy what they do not need, because whatever people truly need they will find without advertising if it is obtainable. Personally, I have been very moved by concepts presented in his chapter entitled How We Turn Into Our Images. He laments that most of us give little importance to the fact that other peoples' realities have been implanted in our consciousness, and suggests that perhaps we have lost touch with our own image-creating abilities, what role they play in our lives and the critical functions they serve. It appears we do not understand the consequences of other people's images replacing our own or being assimilated as equal. Mr. Mander considers the most frightening aspect of television the fact that it intervenes between individuals and their own image-creating abilities and their images of the physical world outside of their own minds. I heartily agree, and am troubled to think that many people operate daily on assumptions drawn from images and portrayals that are inaccurate, exaggerated or blatantly false. I will leave this marvelous book by mentioning a cogent remark made by Robert Keeshan, television's beloved Captain Kangeroo, in which he simply states that all time spent in front of the television is time spent not doing other things. If you were a friend of mine, you would have already received a copy of this missal, since I have purchased over 40, and given them as gifts for all meaningful occasions.

Why should you care about being in the real world all the time? Why force yourself to continuously face the raw here and now? If life were more joyous, wouldn't you want to be in it as much as you could? My friends, you are constantly putting yourselves through harrowing and traumatic events, but make-believe ones. Pseudo-life. You want to escape? Why not make our world a more pleasant place, so we have no desire to avoid it? Living in fantasy does not change reality.

Do you know what it feels like to be a non-plugged in person relating to the television-influenced world? When you describe a firsthand experience it is often affirmed or countered with information given on the tube. References are constantly made to fictitious characters or scenarios and the speaker is dismayed when you don't know what he/she is talking about. Descriptions of actual life occurrences are frequently spoken of as comparable to those portrayed in invented scripts.

My Sisters and Brothers – see the error of your ways! That machine has no power over you if you turn it off. Save your minds. Come back to the true world that you can see, hear, touch, smell and taste for yourself. Redemption is at hand if only you will accept that nothing on that screen is really happening right now in your life.

Amen.

Chapter 14

Reports from the Regions
The Second Staff Meeting

The second staff meeting was held in Kansas City. Jeffrey, Adrian, Jeni, and Amma Mama (Waaaaaah, all the staff cried) did not attend, so we were 11. Mark, Cathy, Tina (staying with a friend), and I (staying at my parents) were local; the rest were housed at a Holiday Inn, partly owned by one of my cousins (a different one, any surprise?). The first day was spent on a tour of the apartment complex that was to become Cooperation House, checking out Northeast Bowl, with whom we were in the midst of contract negotiations, visiting some art projects that Storytellers had done in various city neighborhoods, and meeting with five Storytellers' youth who were interested in becoming part of our first training group.

Day Two, held in a conference room at the Holiday Inn, was a full-day training, mostly run by Oliver and Stacey, but a few sessions by Stef on some theories and techniques of counseling, crisis management, and recognizing potentially violent behavior. Stacey gave us a solid harm reduction background; Oliver shared training tips. That night we went to a Kansas City Royals baseball game.

Day Three the regions gave their reports. What fun! We laughed, told anecdotes of things that had happened with particular youth or groups we had approached, and generally uplifted one another by recounting the remarkable interest we had consistently encountered in our project. Myriam gave an animated account of her experience with a Hispanic group working with gangs in L.A. where she had gone to distribute brochures and applications. She had left her business card and some brochures with the Director and the next day got a call from a youth who asked if she would return to the office to give him and his brother an interview. Out of curiosity, she went to meet the youth, intending to explain how the procedure was going to work, initial receipt of applications, holding a large general meeting for all applicants to more fully explain the project, then at that time set up interviews. She walked in to find the youth, and 14 of his relatives waiting to greet her -- from grandpa down to his 11 or 12 year old brother, who someone had given an oversized business suit to wear. Grandpa was actually not that old, in his late 60's, and stated he was a "carpintero de primera clase" (first class carpenter), and wanted to work for us. The youngest brother wanted to help cleaning up our contruction sites. Five or six of his cousins, brothers, uncles, were actually in our targeted age group, so they were given applications. The original youth commented, "This is only part of my family."

James said he ran out of applications the first day he distributed them at Streetwork. Everybody agreed we were going to be inundated with applications, and did we want to consider raising the number of initial trainees. After lengthy discussion we decided that no, for our first time we had to stay at 100, more or less.

Ernie told us the tale of Katarina, a youth in Miami, who was intent on becoming one of our first collective members. Her story is so poignant it deserves a chapter all its own. By this time he had begun calling Stacey, Stacela (since her singing group was called "Kackâla"), Mark was Mack the Hammer, Tina was B.T. (The word "tina" means bathtub in Spanish, thus B.T.), Cathy was Felix (Cathy's nickname, from her initials, was Cat, so you know, Felix the Cat), James was Jay-YPC (I guess a playoff on Jay-Z, the rapper), and Myriam was Myri Myri quite contriry (oh Ern, give me a break). The rest of the staff had a respite from his cleverness. For now.

Day Four was training again. Oliver laid out the order of topics for the 11 remaining weeks of the summer, after orientation, and stated he had built in three (one per month) mid-week days that were to be music/art creativity, just to break things up for the kids. Oliver and Stacey led two trainings for the staff, so we could experience what the youth would, and they agreed to go to different regions and give individualized instruction to staff who felt they needed it. Each topic was reviewed, and the proposed training methodology was discussed and slightly modified.

Day Five, held on the patio of my parents' house, was a discussion of our candidate selection process. It was not going to be an easy task. We wanted to let everybody in, but knew we couldn't. In this first group we needed youth who could stick with the program, many who had leadership qualities (for they would become role models for subsequent groups), and those who could grasp and incorporate the concepts we were promoting. People brought up specific examples of actual youth, read some applications, and talked about what we wanted to communicate in our all-applicant meetings. We role played some interviews and Oliver kept us on our toes with his rendition of a transgender youth who wondered if he/she could wear platform shoes to work and an "ex-con" who perceived all our policies as, "like they do it in the half-way house."

We all had three weeks to make the final candidate selection. Each region had the autonomy to make their choices and inform headquarters, where Adrian had set up a system to process the data. Tina would arrange transportion (bus tickets and schedules to Springfield, Ohio) for all youth and figure out a shuttle system to get the kids to campus. It was tight, but we were going to do it. Mark was returning to Antioch, where the students had been doing a marvelous job of getting things ready for us. Ernie had found some great deals on sheetrock, paint, wood paneling and light fixtures.

That night we ate at Gates Barbeque and went to a jazz club downtown. Kansas City is famous for both.

I almost forgot. Cathy informed us that Storytellers and YPC received the four other grants we requested. Hot dog! Now the staff could have full-time salaries and benefits.

Chapter 15

Katarina Escapes the Navy

I have known Katarina since she was 19 years old; she is now 24. Her mother, a songwriter and PhD in psychology, is the sister of a friend of mine in Costa Rica. Katarina is a smart, artistic, adventurous, vegetarian, hippie sort. She was born in Mexico but has lived quite a bit in the States and is a permanent resident. When I first met her she had a Chilean boyfriend, was trying to go to community college, and worked at Victoria's Secret (which Ernie calls "Victoria Secretes"). From the earliest stages of the Youth Peace Collective, I told Katarina about the idea and she was anxious to join. But as you know, our time frame delayed, and she traveled in and out of the country a couple times without finding any direction for her life, before we had the good fortune to get funded.

A Navy recruiter got a hold of her. He explained that she would be taught computers and other skills, sent to Hawaii, paid $2,500/month and then given financial help for college when she completed her service. No way she'd ever have to go to war. It sounded like a great opportunity, and her stepfather, who fondly remembered his days of discipline and "compañerismo" (companionship/comradeship) in the army, greatly encouraged her. She had nothing else going. Why not?

So she signed up for the Navy. This was around June and she wasn't scheduled to enter Basic Training until March 4th of the next year. Some of us, her friends, were horrified and bemused. Katarina was one of the most "pacific" young people we knew. Oliver, who had hung out with her in Miami, said, "What in the world is she doing?" Time went on, drawing closer to her entry date and she was still saying that she was content with her decision and wanted to go. " It will be a learning experience for me," she proclaimed.

For awhile I lost track of Katarina because I was making frequent trips to Kansas City and she went to Mexico, for a final fling, to see her sister, year old niece, father and grandmother. She partied in Cancun (where she had lived for awhile as a child), visited D.F. (she's a "chilanga" – native of the capital), and went with her sister and two friends to the desert and did peyote. Wow. What a spiritual experience she had.

The rest of this story Katarina told me in a car going from North Bay Village to Sergio's restaurant on Coral Way. By then it was all over, and we were seeing each other after a three month hiatus.

She returned to Miami from Mexico a few days before she was to be picked up by her recruiter to go to registration for Basic Training. She stayed with friends, a lesbian couple, and visited all her old haunts. On Sunday night, before her fateful Monday appointment, they all smoked marijuana. All Sunday and Sunday night she was feeling scared, like she didn't want to go, and she thought the Navy wasn't really for her. Her Chilean ex-boyfriend told her to call the recruiter in the morning (he was coming at 5:30 a.m.) and tell him she had changed her mind. What could they do to her? " Just tell them you aren't going," he counseled her. The recruiter called Sunday afternoon. She told him she was scared and he told her not to be. Everything would be okay.

The next morning, according to her, she put it all in God's hands. "God, if you want this to happen, let it happen. But if you don't, then stop it." The recruiter came at 5:30 and once again she told him how worried she felt. He tried to assuage her fears. "It will be fine." Not able to contain herself, she confessed about her "drug usage" the night before. She was petrified they'd give her a drug test and then she's be in real trouble. He told her that she wouldn't be tested until she got to training in Chicago and that it was best to say nothing about it. They got to the location; she doesn't really remember where it was, maybe Davie. She was put in a room with a lot of other kids – that's what she called them, young kids, mostly around 18, and none of them looked like her. "They were all kind of nerdy," she remarked. She overheard two boys conversing next to her. "Wouldn't it be cool if we were in Iraq and this big bomb dropped and blasted a whole army unit of those dudes?" and they laughed. "What am I doing here?" she asked herself. They gave her bunches of paperwork to fill out, and the final page said that you are swearing that everything you say is true and if we find out it's not you're going to have big problems (fines, jail, who knows). One question asked if your medical condition had changed or if you'd done any drugs recently, or something like that. She lied and wrote no. Then a person came into the room and said, "I'm Officer So and So and you're joining the Navy and that's serious and we don't put up with any disrespect and you'll follow orders," and on and on like that. They were shuttled to another room, told to wait, and a commanding officer came in and told them how serious the pages they had just signed were, and if anyone had anything they wanted to tell them about the information on those sheets, they should do it now.

All during this time Katarina wanted to stop the process and say, "No, I can't do this." But she couldn't get up the nerve, so she kept moving along with it.

Then came the crucial moment: the swearing-in. She had to take the oath to defend the flag and the nation and follow what the president said and blah, blah, blah. She swore with her right hand and crossed her fingers on her left hand. "What have I done now?" she realized. "I'm screwed."

Immediately after the swearing-in they moved them to a different room, lined them up in military stance, began barking orders, and reprimanded a kid who walked in one minute late. Then they told them they had 7 minutes to get lunch and they'd better be punctual and "You're in the Navy now." All the adults had suddenly started acting really mean.

After lunch they were sitting in another one of their many waiting periods, and Katarina was dying inside. "How can this be happening to me? I know this isn't right. I've got to do something. It's now or never," is what was going through her mind. Her account is that at that very moment she felt God take her hand and pull her up out of her chair and walk her to the commanding officer at the front of the room. "Sir," she said. "I need to speak with you about something very important." "Yes," he snapped. "What is it?" The confession came out. "I lied on my form. I smoked marijuana last night." "WHAT? Why didn't you put it down? Why did you take the oath?" He couldn't believe what he was hearing. "I was scared," was the truth she told.

For a minute he didn't respond. Then he said, as if delivering a terrible blow, " You know now you can never join any branch of the armed services." Yea, she thought, exactly what I wanted. "I don't know what we're going to do with you because you took the oath and you're in the Navy now. I've got to consult with my superiors. Come with me." The others watched her walk out of the room.

A lightness came over her, she told me. A huge sense of relief. He took her to an office and had her sit in the waiting room. He came out of a consultation with another officer and told her they weren't sure what the result of this would be, that it had never happened to them before and that since she was still part of the Navy she might have to work for them in their office. They took her to see a higher officer and she explained her situation again and told them, "I guess this shows I didn't really want to go in because if I really had, I wouldn't have risked it by smoking marijuana." They had her continue sitting in the waiting room. The most surprising thing she noticed was that now all of the people, soldiers and officers, were really nice to her, joking and teasing. "You're ours now, Katarina. We're going to make you work here with us." And "Hey, you're really putting them through it. They've never dealt with this situation before."

Amazing, she thought, maybe I'll even come out of it with a job.

The first commanding officer returned. "Well, Katarina, you are definitely out, (Yes!) so sign these papers, but you have to call me tomorrow because we're still not sure if we have to keep you here working with us or what." She ran into her original recruiter, who noted the situation and asked, a tad horrified, "What happened?" She shrugged her shoulders, "I couldn't do it." Another recruiter who had an errand in Miami drove her home. Upon leaving, one of the youth who had been in the group with her all day, called out as he saw her walking away, "Hey, aren't you going with us?" "No," she replied. "You're lucky," was his retort.

She called the next day and the officer said it had been decided she was completely relieved of service and that she needed to come in and sign papers to that effect. "A miracle," she decided. "I thought they would send me to three months of rehab and then put me in Basic Training."

That's the story of how Katarina escaped the Navy and became one of our first, most staunch, youth collective members. Thanks, God.

Chapter 16

$

I'm not going to waste any of your time accounting for how we spent every penny of our money, if we had enough to cover personnel and operating expenses, what about the rising costs of construction, etc. You must have confidence in me, Michael, Jeffrey, and an accountant we used. One of my shelter staff in New York used to tell me I was addicted to dollar stores, so you can be sure I'm not squandering money. Those first grants were the only ones we ever had to seek because I devised a fund-raising campaign that was to support us forever. You'll see.

Chapter 17

YPC buys Northeast Bowl
¡Qué karma!

Not only did we buy Northeast Bowl, we bought the building across Elmwood street that used to belong to my grandfather. Long ago it housed a ballroom upstairs and a skating rink downstairs. When I was five or six, I had a roller skating birthday party there. Now it was empty – big cavernous spaces. We were going to create YPC regional offices upstairs, and downstairs, jointly with Storytellers, make a coffee house/art center.

The deal closed a couple weeks before summer training. Since Cathy and other Storytellers' staff were going to be summer trainers and work crew leaders, we decided to hold off all work on the property until mid-September, after everyone's two week vacation. Our first projects would be renovation of The Lanes and creation of "The Art Cafe." Cooperation House would be in existence too, but luckily we didn't have to do renovations there. We had enough work for all one hundred youth, if they made it through training.

Did we really think 100 kids, the majority found through programs working with high risk, formerly drug addicted, homeless, and "ex-convict" youth, who had never met one another and came from all parts of the country, could work, live and learn peace together? Could they renovate the Antioch Inn?

We were soon to find out.

Oh, I want to show you the logo Jeni created for The Lanes.

The Lanes

Northeast

Chapter 18

Storytellers Tell Their Stories

Fred: Never knew my parents. Was in a lot of group homes, in juvie a couple times. Was a pretty troubled kid, used to steal cars and shit, but with master keys I made myself. "You're too smart for your own good," I was told all the time. Yeah, so smart that I figured out how to watch people put in their ATM pin numbers, in a minute I could catch the card numbers and code, had a friend who made these fake cards that worked, and I stole a lot of money. Was in jail for four years. Came out, and what was I supposed to do? I'm a young black male with a record. You tell me. I shoulda fucking been an inventor.

Lawannie: People look at me and just see a fat girl. They don't know who I am inside. I been raped so many times you wouldn't believe it. Started when I was eight, my uncle. Then at school by two big boys. For about a year by one of my mom's stupid boyfriends, and when I told her she slapped me and said, "Shut your mouth. That man puts food on this table." I was 14 then. Now they got me on all these meds. I tried to kill myself lots of times. Look at all these cuts on my arm. I even got raped by a damn attendant in the mental hospital when I was so out of it I didn't know what was happening except I figured it out when I saw my undies torn and felt this sticky shit on my pussy. Sometimes I pray to god to please make me die. I must be a bad person for all this stuff to happen to me.

Miguel: Always I saw my Dad beat up my mom when he got drunk. I loved my mom, so when I got big enough I stood up to him with a bat, and said, hit her one more time hijo de puta and I kill you. That's when he kicked me out, and she said I'd better go, cause I had 6 little brothers and sisters and she didn't know what else to do. My Tia Alicia took care of me till I was 17 then she got married and her husband didn't want me either. So I went to my cousins in Mexico, but nothing was happening there, no work, and they just smoked weed, sniffed this glue shit and robbed rich people's houses. Two of my primos are rotting in jail down there right now. I came back, had to, and lucked out finding a job at a carwash. I rent a room in this old lady's house. She's okay, the vieja makes great tamales.

Chapter 19

The First Summer Training

Black, White, Asian, Hispanic, Native American, and Arabic youth came from 23 states. They arrived over the weekend, mostly on Sunday, and the cafeteria was open, but no activities were planned except a "Meet and Greet with Refreshments" in the Caf from 8-10 p.m. both nights. Youth were free to roam around campus and town, relax, and acclimate. All activities would begin Monday at 9 a.m. Along with room assignments (arbitrarily pre-selected double room occupancy), each individual was given a copy of the schedule for the first week. Breakfast was 7:30 - 9:00 a.m. At nine everyone was expected to be in the Caf for Morning Announcements. Staff had already been at Antioch for a few days for meetings and final planning, and during arrival weekend we wandered around making ourselves available for questions, predicaments, unhappinesses and the like. They could distinguish staff because we were the only ones at that moment wearing light blue t-shirts with the YPC Logo over the heart. Each year would have a different color; blue was picked first.

The next morning I gave Announcements. I told the group that before noon everyone was to find their Work Crew on lists that were posted on various walls, get five YPC t-shirts from their Crew leaders, and spend the rest of the time in "getting-to-know-you" activities with their crew. Prior to coming, everyone had been informed that YPC "uniform" was a YPC t-shirt and pants or shorts at least to the middle of the thigh. After lunch we would have an explanation from Mark and Ernie about the nature of the work we were going to perform in our "labor of peace," and then Oliver and Stacey would describe the upcoming trainings. Lots of time would be allowed for questions. I called up each one of the "Coordinators," introduced them and they said a few words. Amma Mama got up too, explained Amma, told them where she was setting up shop – her chair and table would be in one of the dorm rooms – and informed them they had to sign up for massages, no walk-ins. Her hours were from 5 - 9 p.m. on weekdays and from 10 a.m. - 2 p.m. on weekends. Staff had separate times. I informed everyone that after dinner I was going to give a little welcoming speech, then there would be a dance deejayed by hip hop anthropologist cousin, who, along with his wife, was part of our additional summer staff.

Thankfully someone recorded my speech that night, because I was so emotional I have no recollection what I said. Apparently (the tape wouldn't lie) this was it: "This is a thrilling and monumental day for me, as I hope it is for all of you. I thank you for being here, for sharing our belief in peace and for being willing to put your heart, soul, mind, and physical strength into creating a peaceful world. As you sit here, war is taking place in other parts of the world. Maybe we cannot stop war right now, but we can plant the seeds, which are ideas, convictions, and actions, that will some day make armed conflict a thing of the past. All of us (I wave a hand towards all the staff standing near me) believe in all of you. We are here for you. Please come to any one of the staff when you need any kind of assistance. And if you can catch me, I'm usually going 90 miles per hour (they laugh), I'll be happy to help you too. I love you. Peace." Then I made the peace sign. And you can hear it on the tape, someone from the audience yelled "Peace." and then all different voices were calling Peace, Peace, Peace, Peace, Peace, Peace, Peace. Each youth stood up as they called out. I was frozen in my spot, staring and listening. Peace, Peace, Peace, in one hundred unique voices. My emotions overflowing, I quickly left the Caf. As I ran out, I heard the turntables start with a song I love by Wyclef Jean, "Just cause she dances fo' folk, that don't make her a ho, no..." and that really made me cry.

The next four days were spent in mornings of participatory workshops on theoretical topics related to collective living, communication, mediation and the sources of violence. The youth were divided in groups of ten, not their work crew, but in a fashion that by the end of the week most people would have been in a group with nearly everyone else. The afternoons were lectures and practical demonstrations by our carpenters, architect, some work crew leaders, and an electrician. One afternoon we talked about the technique we wanted to try out in case any potentially violent conflicts ever arose between two people or a group. If someone saw an argument that was starting to get overheated, they were to call, "POW WOW!" Every other youth and staff collective member in the area was to immediately come over and make a circle around the individuals arguing. All the youth knew that if anybody ever threw a blow, they would be on the bus home that same day. The pow wow circle provided protection and witnesses. The idea was to de-escalate the argument as quickly as possible. The actual matter in dispute would subsequently be brought to the "collective council," which would be formed in the second week. This technique is not unique to YPC. I think I heard about it being used in one of those wilderness camps for troubled teens.

What can I tell you about our youth collective members? They were all shapes and sizes and natures of personality. Two of them were foster mom cousin's former foster kids. A few of them were children of friends of mine. One was Oliver's niece. Most were youth who would have considered the military, if they could have tolerated the authoritarianism, the best option life was ever going to present them. They saw this experience as a combination of camp, college, and job corps. The whole vibe of YPC was novel and fascinating to them; I could tell. Thomas lifted me up in a hug one day and said, "This is so cool. Everybody is nice. I can't believe it."

It would take the rest of this book for me to describe blow by blow what happened at summer training, so I'm going to pick some significant occurrences to exemplify how we dealt with things. Before that let me say that Monday of week two we asked any youth who wanted to be on "collective council" to put their name in a hat. We picked out five names. Staff did the same, and we picked two names. Those council members would serve for one week, and the selection would take place each subsequent Monday. No one could serve twice, that way lots of people got the chance to serve in the capacity of arbiters of disagreements. A good lesson in democracy.

First I will tell you about something that happened the third week of training. It was about 9:30 p.m. one weekday night and I was walking on the second floor of the dorm to inform one youth that her mother had called and needed to speak to her immediately. This girl was actually the daughter of my oldest, closest childhood friend in K.C., the person who had *shared* a swing with me as a child, so you know how far back I'm talking. I had known her daughter from birth. As I approached the room a certain odor was clearly detectable in the hallway. Mota! (Mexican slang for marijuana) Trust me; I know the smell. I knocked on the door and opened it without waiting for a response. I stuck my head in and said, "Sheena, your mother wants you to call her right away," closed the door and walked out. My heart was pounding and all I wanted to do was get away as quickly as possible. I went to find whoever I could of the staff to "pow wow." Inside the room I had seen Katarina (shocked?), Thomas and Mimi of Streetwork fame, Mohammed from New Jersey, Javier from Miami and of course, Sheena.

I found Oliver, Tina, Gail, Stef and James, and dragged them into my room, explaining the situation and asking, "What now?" We all decided that the first thing we were going to do was wait and see what the youth were going to do. They had been clearly busted, but how would they react? I had not reprimanded or said a word to them about what I saw, and smelled, but everyone knew they had broken a basic rule: No drugs or alcohol in Youth Peace Collective living and working locations. What they did in town or off campus in their free time was their own business, provided they didn't have run-ins with the law. That was the harm reduction philosophy; behaviorally based and without judgments. If you completed your work, training, and community commitments responsibly, your personal lifestyle choices were not questioned. But for legal reasons, we did have certain rules.

We had been sitting in my room for about 45 minutes when there was a knock on my door. "Come in." Mimi and Thomas walked in. They looked around at everybody, handed me a letter and walked out, without saying a word. The letter read, "Janet. We're sorry. We know what we did is wrong but you know we're a bunch of pot heads. Please don't send us home. We love it here. We will take any consaquences [sic] you want to give us." It was in Mimi's handwriting, and signed by everyone present.

The next day I took the letter to Stacey and Mark, who were the staff on "collective council" that week. I told them I wanted to call a meeting of the council and all the offenders. The meeting was held that afternoon after work. The dejected youth sat in chairs facing council members sitting behind a long table. Laquisha, one of the council members, said, "Okay you guys. What do you have to say for yourselves?" They were all quiet until Thomas jumped out of his chair and cried, "It was wrong. It was wrong. What can we say? We all knew it was wrong, but we did it anyway. Shoot us. I mean, we're sorry. There's nothing we can do. Just tell us what's going to happen now." "No one else has anything else they want to say?" Billy, another council member, asked. There was silence.

The council told the culprits to wait outside and they would be called in when a decision was reached. In ten minutes, Chen Shu from the council, brought pens and paper to the youth and told each one to write what they thought should happen to them in this case. He'd come back in 15 minutes to get the sheets. Meanwhile the council discussed various options, but withheld decision until they saw what the youth themselves were going to come up with. The papers came in: 1) Make us clean all the toilets in the dorms; 2) Make us plant some trees. Since we smoked up some trees, we should plant some more. Ha, ha. Really, I'll do anything. 3) I don't care what happens as long as you don't tell my mom or make us watch hours of Just Say No movies. 4) Make us apologize to the whole group and ask them what they think should happen to us. 5) I am willing to do whatever you order me to. I like it here and want to keep working. 6) We could wash the floors and walls of the Caf because it's kind of grungy. The council had come up with a few ideas of its own.

The next morning at Announcements Mark got up and said he wanted to tell the community about an incident that had come before the collective council and how it was dealt with. He explained the situation and handed down the sentence: "All six of these indivduals will be confined to campus this upcoming weekend, and during that time they will be required to wash the floors and walls of the Caf and give the walls a new coat of paint. They are also required to apologize to the community." He called each name out and they stood up and said "Sorry." "Furthermore, they are publicly informed that if they have two more infractions of Collective rules, they will be asked to leave." Mimi came up and gave me a hug as she walked to join her work crew.

Aren't you kind of curious what the staff collective finally resolved about the television issue? We turned one dorm room into a "TV Room," with pillows all over the floor. At least if the kids were going to watch, they'd be together, and would have to come to a collective decision on what channel. All summer long I would randomly stop in to see how crowded it was, and it was virtually always empty. Most common was to find a couple in there, usually making out.

The second situation I wish to recount has to do with a pregnancy. Belinda, a 22 year old from L.A. had been stuck like glue from the first day of training to a young man from Hawaii named Arthur, we called him Artie. In late July Belinda confided to Myriam that she was pregnant. Myriam came to me. I went to the staff. The staff took it to the youth collective (it had already become public knowledge because Artie told some people). For three nights running, after dinner until 10 p.m. we talked about the issue: What should happen to a collective member who becomes pregnant? What should happen to the person who got her pregnant? And how were we going to be able to know for sure who it was? The last question was an easy one in the particular case of Belinda and Artie, but many of the youth were aware that if certain people got pregnant, the answer might not be so clear. It wasn't about DNA tests and things like that; it was about honor and honesty.

I was a main proponent of adopting the rule that anyone who became pregnant and her mate (whoever it ended up being) should be asked to leave. My theory was: there were condoms everywhere and all the youth were well aware of safe sex. I was not against sex and babies, per se, but the time spent in the Youth Peace Collective was not the moment to be engendering new human beings. Not even mentioning diseases, if someone was irresponsible enough to get pregnant (both parties), then they are not showing the level of maturity necessary for YPC. If they meant to get pregnant, well then go and begin setting up life to raise your child. I didn't mean to sound mad, but I just felt like the youth should be responsible sexually and focus their energies on this once in a lifetime experience. Don't muddle it with morning sickness and hormone swings, and some of the work we were doing could be dangerous for a pregnant woman. As for the male component of the equation, I felt they should be held equally culpable and receive the same consequences. As you can imagine, opinions were many and varied on the subject, and heated.

Near the end of the second night of discussion, with similar opinions on both sides being repeated over and over because absolutely everybody wanted to be heard and that's the collective way, some youth started to get angry and aggressive. I was called a fascist. One young woman from Oakland said that if YPC ever made a rule like the one I proposed, she'd take us to court and "sue the hell" out of us for discrimination. A female voice yelled out, "WHAT DO YOU WANT US TO BE, A BUNCH OF NUNS?" and then Reynolds, from Portland, Maine stormed out of the room saying,

"Fuck this shit." At the moment he did that Amma Mama jumped up and interjected, "Have you heard the one about the two guys who go out for a walk and they see a dog licking its balls. The one guy says, 'I wish I could do that,' and the second guy says, 'Don't you think you ought to pet the dog first?'" There was a collective moan, and then everybody started laughing. Stef suggested finishing up the discussion the following night and that collective council would present some specific recommendations to the group.

Here were the recommendations: 1) Any youth peace collective female who becomes pregnant while on training will be allowed to finish training, but will not be asked to join YPC. 2) The father of the baby, same as above. 3) If a woman gets pregnant during her YPC 6-month stint, she will be asked to leave after her third month of pregnancy due to medical reasons. 4) The father of the baby can either: leave when the baby's mother does or finish his stint and half of the sum owing to him at the end of the six months will go to the mother of the baby.

After three final hours of volatile debate, the recommendations were adopted with the addition of one point. 5) If it is unclear who the father of the baby is, all sexual partners of the pregnant female will take consequences noted in #2 and #4. Subsequent to that meeting, more jars full of condoms were placed around, and I noticed they were being actively taken.

Renovations of the Inn and Union went well. The youth stripped and hauled, hammered and sanded, cleaned and painted. Bright, unusual colors were selected for many of the Union office rooms. The Inn walls were painted softer colors, and in a few rooms murals were created by groups of talented youth, similar to what they've done at the Carlton Arms Hotel, the "art hotel" in New York. A group of ten youth who had expressed special interest, were learning to install new lighting in the Inn. The system of having the youth participate in community maintenance was working smoothly. There were 25 jobs to be done (like dishwashers, cooks helpers, clean up the Caf, dorm hallway and communal bathroom cleanliness, runners for Staff, etc.) so every youth had one week out of the month that all week they did their community job instead of going to work. Oliver and Stacey felt that Friday trainings were proceeding excellently, and that the youth were gaining depth and understanding of the sources of violence.

In the evenings the kids often gathered behind Main Building playing guitar and singing, cutting open a watermelon, telling jokes and smoking cigarettes. A dorm room had been set aside and dubbed, "Mellow Meditation." It was a quiet spot, where anyone could sit and think amidst incense and candles. Stacey did acupuncture in individuals' rooms, Myriam and Ernie ran a poetry writing workshop, Cathy and the Storytellers folks along with youth were designing the murals, James had a posse that worked out with him nightly, and Tina and Jeni held a group called, "Discovering your Spiritual Self." Amma Mama's schedule was always packed. Often in the dorm rooms there were three or four kids hanging out, talking and listening to music. Most youth went to bed before midnight, though there was no "lights out" time. They were tired.

The final incident I'm going to tell you about was the one and only time all summer we had to call "POW WOW." The accounts I have are from Mark, Gail, and hip-hop anthropologist cousin, all of whom were observers in some part. About 10:30 one night Gail and hip-hop and his wife were sitting in the lounge area of one of the dorms chatting with four or five kids. They started to hear yelling and door slamming from down the hall. They ran down the hallway just as someone screamed "POW WOW!!!!!" When they got to the scene, they heard two roommates going at it. "You goddamn idiot. I can't believe this. I'm going to kill you. You ruined my best fucking shirt. Look at it, you asshole. Two burns. You motherfucker, you fucked up my shirt." The other guy was saying, "Hey man, sorry..." "Sorry my ass. I lend you my shirt and," the first boy was saying when the other cut in, "Hey, what's the big deal asshole, I'll buy you another one." "What's the big deal? WHAT'S THE BIG DEAL?" the first boy yelled just when Gail stepped in and said "Stop it you guys. Stop it right now. Either come out here in the hall or we're all coming in there to make a circle around you." By that time there were 8 or 10 other kids in the hall. "Get out of my face," one of the boys said to Gail. Hip-hop countered, "Hey now, watch it," and everybody made their way into the room and surrounded the boys. It wasn't the best scenario because the room was cramped, adding to the pressure of the situation. " Let me out of here," the boy who had burned the shirt said as he tried to push his way out, but the circle interlocked arms and wouldn't let him through. "What exactly happened," Gail tried to ask in a calming tone. "This motherfucker burned my best shirt," whined the aggrieved party. "Fuck you," said the other kid, "I told you I'd buy you a new one." "Well, where are you going to get it, asshole. My uncle brought this back for me from Italy." "It doesn't look Italian to me; it looks like you got it at K-Mart." This type of repartee was going on when Mark showed up at the door. "What the hell is happening in here?" Someone quickly gave him the gist of the argument, both disputants still encircled by the group. He walked inside the circle and said, "Show me the shirt. Jesus, yeah, this shirt is fucked up. How did it happen?" The burner said, "Hey man, you know, it was an accident. I was kinda fucked up and smoking a cig and..." Mark: "So you borrow a dude's shirt, and I gotta say this is a nice shirt, and get yourself fucked up and then boom, the next thing you know the shirt has burn holes. What would you do if this happened to your best shirt, the one someone brought you as a special gift?" The kid responded, "I guess I'd be really pissed." Mark: "Yeah, and that's what he (pointing to the other guy) is. So what are you going to do to make it right?" The kid, "I don't know. What can I possibly do? Do you think the burns can be fixed?" Mark: "No man, I don't think so." Kid: "So what can I do? I can't go to fucking Italy and buy him a new one." Mark to the other boy, "So he can't go to fucking Italy and buy you a new one. What do you want him to do?" Other boy: "I don't know. Damn, I loved that shirt and my uncle gave it to me. It's just not fair. He shouldn't have been so careless." Mark: I know man, it's a bitch, somebody fucks up your best thing. Why did you let him wear it? Answer: "Hey man, he's my roommate and he asked me for it, you know." Mark: "Yeah, I know, and that was nice of you man, but when you lend something to someone, sometimes things happen, they fuck it up. Best not to lend your favorite things, ya know." That was kind of how the "mediation" went until one of the kids in the circle said, "Hey Mark, why doesn't he just fucking buy him a new shirt, even if it isn't exactly the same, don't you think that's fair?" Mark: "Yeah, actually I do think that's pretty fair. Okay dude, this weekend you're going with me into Springfield and we're buying the nicest shirt we can find that maybe looks something like this one, and that isn't cheap shit, and it's on your dime, and I will tell Community Council that's what we did to resolve this. Agreed, you two?" They nodded. Mark: "Okay, shake." They shook hands. Mark: "It's over, now get me out of this circle because I'm starting to feel fucking claustrophobic."

Are you exhausted just hearing about summer training? We, the staff I mean, were wiped out after it was over and anxiously looking forward to two weeks vacation. I need to tell you a couple final things, but I'll save them for the next chapter.

Chapter 20

Final Selection and The Skit

In the last week of training we explained that it was time for the collective to select who was going to be part of our first Youth Peace Collective group, to work in Kansas City creating The Lanes, Cooperation House and The Art Cafe. Each youth and staff was given a "ballot" on which they were to write the name of any trainee they felt had exemplified behavior inconsistent with the goals and philosophies of YPC. If any individual, personally, did not want to continue with the project, he or she should write "Self Select Out" and put their name, otherwise the ballots were anonymous. If a name was written on 20 or more ballots, that person would not be invited into YPC. It wasn't an unpopularity contest, or trying to exclude anybody; it was about giving an honest evaluation. Anyone with more than 20 notations, would be "deferred," and could try again next summer. The Final Selection would be announced the last night of training.

Don't get nervous. No one was "deferred." There were five or six names that showed up on 8 or 9 ballots and 7 youth self selected out. One of them was the young woman from Oakland, whom we later heard was having a baby. Two kids were going to school in the fall, two said they might join later but didn't want to right now, and two said it was too much work for them.

The final night we had our "Celebration." First the President of Antioch spoke and said that the renovations were more wonderful than their wildest dreams, that students, faculty and administration of Antioch thanked us profoundly, enjoyed having our lively spirits grace their campus, and looked forward to a long and fruitful collaboration with YPC. Then I spoke, and don't even ask me what I said because I basically did nothing but bawl that whole night. I do remember though, thanking our first "anonymous" funder and saying that without their belief in us, this never could have happened. Thanks also went to the four other foundations and Antioch. I'm sure I must have praised the youth and staff for their remarkable work. James read off everyone's name and they all came up front and received an envelope with $1,500 in cash – compensation for three months of hard work, training and living peacefully. After each name he said either YPC, or Self Selected. During the whole name reading everyone was on their feet, applauding.

Then came the skit. I hadn't even known about it until a couple of days prior. They wanted to keep it a secret from me, too. It was the "Coordinators'" gift to the youth, a skit called: YPC Takes Over the World. I hope I can do it justice, because it was hysterical. Here's my best description of how it went.

Tina came out in a hugely outrageous wig, I could tell trying to approximate my hair, except hers was green. She said, "Let it be clear to all of you and make no mistake. The world will be liberated. For its own good, we are taking over the world. We will try not to put any of you in harm's way and there may be some collateral damage, but we must protect our freedom. The freedom to shop." Then Gail, Stef, Myriam, Stacey, Jeni and Cathy came out dressed in these crazy outfits made up of long and short skirts, boots, scarves, ponchos, hats, big sweaters – each one totally distinct. They began singing, to the tune of "Going to the Chapel," "We're going to the discount mall and we're gonna get discount clothes ....." and this whole take-off on buying cheap stuff and all the different things they could find at the mall. When they finished they sat off to the side and watched intently, like they were looking at a TV. Oliver walks in and pulls up a chair and sits down very seriously. Then he starts talking really fast. "Welcome to YPC shopping channel. We have some fine bargains for you today starting with a strong, durable shovel, good for digging foundations, gardens or bomb shelters. Sold at the low, low price of $79.90. Buy three you get a flower pot for free. On to another lovely item, a condom holder, fits up to 147 condoms, clear see-through exterior, vacuum sealed going for only $23. Get 'em while they last." All the while he's doing this, Amma Mama is walking around giving little massages to everyone's shoulders. Oliver goes on. "Summer special, one beautiful Italian long sleeved man's shirt, with a couple burn holes in it, going for the unbelievable price of $64. And don't miss the sale of the year, YPC handy toothbrush covers so your toothbrush will never be cold at night and you can distinguish it from everyone else's of the same color, they come in mauve, chartreuse and pale grey with the famous YPC logo on it." At this moment James, Ernie and Mark come out and sing to Oliver, "Stop, in the name of love, before you make me sick. Stop, in the name of love, don't want to buy that shit. Think it oh, oh ver. Think it oh, oh ver." (facing the watching group, wagging their forefingers) Then the Tina character walks in and yells, "What is going on here? I'm not believing this. You jerks haven't bought anything. While you sit there staring at the boob tube, millions of products are being made all over the world and you're not buying anything. This has got to stop. You need these things. You want these things. Go get them." Everybody runs off, Deb is left looking for someone to massage, and she sadly walks off alone. Then they all come back in and stand in a straight line across. They recite this poem, each one saying a line. I made Oliver let me read it later, because I saw his hand in all of this. It went:

We love to laugh, we love to tease,
But you know our mission is bringing peace.
To a world that's filled with hate and war,
Like The Raven we say, "Nevermore." (Ern delivered this with much aplomb.)

You've joined us here all summer long
With workshops, painting and Amma Mom.
We hope you've learned a little bit
And don't think it's all just a crock of shit. (Of course that was Mark's line.)

(here the kids were laughing so hard, they had to wait)

Carry on now in YPC.
Show them our stuff in Kansas City. (Tina accented the 2nd syllable)
We're proud of you, believe in you all,
So let's have peace in the world by fall. (all of them together)

The kids stood up, and for nearly five minutes they clapped, cheered, whistled, hooted, hollered, and somebody yelled out, "Mark, you're the bomb. The atomic bomb!!!"

Hip-hop anthropologist cousin got to the turntables and with a sample of the chorus of "We are the World," he started the music. The kids groaned and laughed. He yelled, "Joke, joke. Just a joke." And immediately broke into Jurassic 5's "Quality Control." The dancing started and lasted far into the night, way beyond when I retired to my room to cry.

Chapter 21

Kansas City Here We Come

Mid-September everyone reunited in K.C. I had spent the "vacation" break there, getting final kinks worked out. The 93 youth with us had signed on for six months. They were housed in apartment cousins' complex and most of them ended up sharing studios because tenants were staying to the end of their leases. Since the apartments were furnished, move-in was easy and we had allowed youth to pick their room-mates, if they expressed that desire. With a construction crew we scrutinized the physical state of Northeast Bowl and found, to our amazement and relief, that it only required superficial renovations – new paint, wall patching and redo the floors. The lanes and bowling equipment were in good shape, and a little kitchen was still functioning. My Dad's old office was intact too. It brought back visions of him sitting in there doing paperwork, smoking his pipe, opening the safe. If the entire crew focused on the bowling alley, we could have it ready in a few weeks and start business. Ern set out to find "bar" tables and stools, three pool tables and two ping-pong. I watched the youth walk around the building, strategizing and suggesting improvements. "Hey Cathy," Thomas called. "Can we paint a huge mural on this wall?" "Definitely," Cathy replied. Mimi added, "Let's create a section of multi-colored bowling balls that we let each little kid who bowls here autograph." Thomas picked Mimi up in a bear hug, "Hon, I'm so glad we're here."

The building that was to house the offices and The Art Cafe was a mess. It was gutted, but full of rubble. After the bowling alley was finished, the group would go over there and begin cleaning up. In the meantime Cathy and Mark looked for an architect and construction company that could incorporate our youth as their helpers. We hired ten more "Coordinators," so the rest of the staff could go back to their respective cities and begin planning for our second training group, which was expanding to 200. Half of the new coodinators were Storytellers' people who had been with us over the summer, plus Dean and Tauno were brought on as work crew leaders.

Cooperation House took awhile to get together. Yes, the youth were all living over there, but everyone was so bushed after their day's work, nobody had the energy to have the all-house meeetings, service committees, and work component written into the initial concept. For the moment YPC hired apartment cousins' maintenance and security crew for the complex, and three of the new coordinators took over the project management, helping resolve roommate difficulties and all other tenant issues. One activity did emerge early on over at Cooperation House, which the youth called "Saturday Nite Jams." From about 7 p.m. to midnight every Saturday night music was set up by the swimming pool – a different person deejaying each weekend. Sometimes there was dancing by the side of the pool, or rap competitions. The last weekend in September, when Kansas City experienced two days of "Indian Summer" (temperatures in the 80's, and the pool still hadn't been drained from the summer) there was a swim-fest. The kids were playing volleyball in the pool when Mohammed started fooling around, pretending like he was a TV reporter with a microphone. "Here we are in sunny Kansas City, Kansas – not Kansas City, Missouri – just two blocks from State Line, and we're going to ask these happy people how they're enjoying this summer weather. Sir...." he said to Reynolds, "Is it HOT enough for you?" Reynolds stared at him, "No," and then jumped in the pool. Then Mohammed changed his tack, and went up to Laquisha. "Excuse me Miss, could you please tell our viewing audience how the Youth Peace Collective has changed your life?" Curiously, she responded seriously. "I never believed in my own abilities before. Now I'm learning so many new things, and it feels good. And it feels good to help people." "And you sir, do you have something to say," he directed to Chen Shu, who responded, "I feel part of a vanguard in my generation, like we're in the forefront of a new emerging idea." Sheena jumped in, "Hi Mom, Dad....I want to say to all of you out there that the Youth Peace Collective teaches us to feel responsibility towards one another. Respect is the word of the day." With that, Thomas grabbed Mohammed from behind and lifted him up, "Hey dude, I'm learning peace, but enough of this" and threw him into the pool.

K.C. was fine. They had a strong team, youth and staff, clearly delineated goals, and enough work to keep everyone occupied. I needed to run back to Miami to put some details in place, and, more importantly, I missed my cortadito and pastelitos.

Chapter 22

Oliver takes his training on the road

All the regions were asking for Oliver's help. Everyone felt one of the criteria for selection of training candidates needed to be participation in a workshop, YPC style. The workshops had been so effective during the summer, Coordinators thought applicants should get a taste of our method, and staff wanted to observe youth in the group dynamic. Each region had unique youth populations and issues, so Oliver decided to spend one week in each selection site, helping folks create appropriate workshops. He would run a few groups to let staff see his technique, then they could modify, as they saw fit. He called his endeavor "Peace Train." During his absence, Stacey, Gail and James held workshops and individual interviews in Rochester, Philadelphia, Pittsburgh, Boston, Newark, Washington, D.C., Baltimore, Hartford, Providence, Manchester, N.H., Burlington, Vermont and Bangor, Maine.

Peace Train chugged first to Miami, and it was like old home week at the Tower; the boys gave Oliver his former room on the third floor. We had received more than 150 applications from kids all over the metro area – Overtown, Opa-locka, Hialeah, Little Haiti, Little Havana, Liberty City, Allapattah, Perrine, Coconut Grove and even a couple from Kendall. We rented a conference room in a hotel near the airport and set appointments for each youth to attend two workshops – held during morning or afternoon sessions. Each workshop group was to have no more than 20 participants – attendance was mandatory for completing the application process. Morning sessions were given a breakfast buffet, and afternoons got cold cuts and salads. We made sure all groups had a mixture of ages (within our range), ethnicities and sexes.

The first workshops were co-facilitated by Oliver and Esmeralda, an Afro-Cuban educator employed by a youth serving agency with whom we had been working closely. The exercise they started with was called "The Box." Ground rules were set up: do not interrupt anyone speaking, no intentionally disrespectful comments, be as honest as you feel comfortable being. Every youth was given a piece of paper that had nothing but the outline of a big square drawn on it. Oliver told the participants, "This is the box that society puts you into, maybe because of your race, sexual orientation, cultural heritage, family values, body type, whatever. It's what the people around you say you must do, or be, or believe. I want each one of you to write the things that are in YOUR box, what you have felt in your life as the commands about what you should be like." The group was given fifteen minutes to write. The chairs in the room had been arranged in a circle, and Esmeralda said, after they finished writing, "We're going to go around the circle and I want each person to stand up, say their name, and read what is inside their box." Out of the twenty youth invited to the session, twelve had come. Here's what was inside the boxes:

Trish: Be pretty and sexy. Don't show how smart you are. Don't mess with Hispanic boys. Find a man with money. Go to church. Help take care of my younger brothers and sisters.

Azziz: Keep our Muslim traditions. Do not marry out of our religion. Be strong and do not show weakness. Study and have a profession. Protect my sisters. Respect my elders.

Julio: Be heterosexual (I'm not. I'm gay.) Go into my dad's business (He owns a car dealership. I'm not interested in that.) Pray to God for my sins. Don't be a wimp.

Connie: Work hard in school so you can get a scholarship. Get married and have babies so my mom can have grandchildren. Don't gain weight, fat is bad. Pretend like my dad is not a raging alcoholic. And act like I don't hear him when he lies to my mom.

Kevin: Never rat out your homeboy. Help my mother. Don't trust white people, they're all prejudiced underneath. Make money, and lots of it. Look sharp. Don't let a girl run your life – show them who's boss.

Consuelo: Be polite and soft-spoken. Help out at home and clean up, even when it's my brothers who make the mess. Do well in school. Be proud of being Nicaraguan. Believe in Jesus and the Virgin Mary. Don't let a man take advantage of you, because then he won't respect you.

Avital: Never forget that you were born an Israeli and that the holocaust could happen again. Money is important, but it isn't everything. Family is the most important thing. Education is the second most important thing. A woman should have her own career.

It is a woman's responsibility to keep the family together.

Arturo: Be a man. Be tough on the outside but gentle inside, especially to children. Be a good provider for your family and don't drink too much. Clothes make the man, and a nice car helps too. Don't forget your Spanish. God bless America.

Evelyn: Stand up for yourself. Be a strong black woman. Don't put up with shit from men. You can be whatever you want to be. Haitians are different from Americans.

Lilanne: Follow the Hindu faith and the teachings of your parents. Have friends from our community. Have compassion for people. Do not dress in a sexual way. Do not be influenced by all the American values.

Rob: Be an upstanding citizen, like vote and pay taxes. Work hard and make money. Marry a nice girl and raise a family. Don't lie or steal. Try to help people in need, but don't be a fool. Don't let people know what you're really thinking.

Reggie: Be cool. Keep it real. Don't let your family down. Find the best gig you can and work it.

"Wow," Oliver said, "How different and interesting all of your boxes are. Look around at each other. Every one of you has different influences in your lives and different assumptions. Now I want to go around the circle again and have each of you say what you felt about other people's boxes, either specifically or in general." Some mentioned feeling sorry for people because of certain pressures, or they identified with a particular comment and one white person said they were sad to hear a black person was told not to trust whites. That led Esmeralda into a little talk about prejudice and discrimination, what causes it, how it gets perpetuated and how you begin dismantling it. The co-facilitators guided the discussion, making sure all participants felt clearly heard and safe to speak their minds. Then the group took a 15 minute break.

The next workshop was called "Solve a Problem Together." The group of twelve was divided into 3 groups of four (by arbitrarily picking numbers out of a hat:1,2,3). Each group was given a "predicament" that supposedly all of them are in together. They were to come out with a group decision of how they would deal with it, with 20 minutes to figure it out. The "problems" were:

1. You've all been to a bar drinking (a bit too much) and you're driving home at 2:30 a.m. The driver of the car turns a corner too sharp and hits the curb hard, blowing a tire. There is no spare and you're in a residential part of town, not near anyone's home.

2. You've gone to the beach together at the end of Key Biscayne. While all four are in the water, one of you gets a fleeting glimpse of somebody bending down over the blanket where all your stuff is sitting. When you get back you see that one person's wallet was taken, their cell phone, and the

keys to the car you have come in, where all the rest of your stuff is locked in the trunk.

3. You are together at an open air concert at Bayside. While you're sitting and listening to the music, somebody behind you makes a disrespectful comment about one of your group, and then keeps making loud, derogatory remarks. Someone from behind flicks the back of the head of the person they have been dissing.

Each group read their scenario and gave the group's decision of how they would deal with it. Other participants were invited to comment on the creativity, practicality, and cooperativeness of the solution. Group members were asked to relate the process they went through in coming to the decision, and explain how they determined the best solution, if there were various competing options. Comments were made like, "We had to take into account everyone's fears and hang-ups," and "It felt good to have other people offering solutions, so I didn't have to figure out everything alone."

At the end of this session Oliver and Esmeralda talked about the level of seriousness and responsibility expected in YPC, the importance of bringing an open mind and willingness to learn to the experience. They were told that no final decisions had been made about who would be accepted into summer training, and that we could not do that until all 150 applicants had been given the chance to come to the workshops. If they were no longer interested in being a candidate, they should inform us, otherwise please wait and they would hear from us one way or the other in about a month, when many of them would be called for a personal interview. We thanked them for their interest and participation.

On the way out I heard a few of the kids' remarks. "Totally cool. I hope I get picked." "That was different. I've never met an Israeli before." "Evelyn, nice to meet you. Any chance I could have your phone number? Maybe we could go out some time." One of the girls went up to Esmeralda and gave her a hug saying, "Thanks for being so understanding."

Each group in Miami had more or less kids, changing ethnic configurations, and the same team-building scenarios played out different ways. Handed out to all attendees, was a list Oliver made of the projected trainings for the summer. He wanted candidates to know what we intended to cover. Here was his list: (after the first week of orientation)

Week 2: Power and Oppression—the "Ism's" Exercise: Step into the circle if this applies to you. Looking at the threads between racism, sexism, adultism, jingoism, etc.

Week 3: Violence – Breaking it Down Overview of sexual, physical, emotional and spiritual violence.

Week 4: Anger and Conflict Resolution Exercise: Lifting the mask, to see what is really underneath the guise of anger and alternative ways to resolve conflicts.

Week 5: Healthy Relationships   Exercises: "The Bad and the Ugly" and My Ideal Mate

Week 6: Sex and Sexuality   Understanding the difference between the two. Exercise: My body, my responsibility.

Week 7: Racism   Individual awareness of its prevalence in society and our lives.

Week 8: Mending Fences   Tools for improving relationships, role playing to illustrate a variety of methods for relating to others.

Week 9: Sexual Orientation and Gender Issues   Including some games to test knowledge of HIV and STD's

Week 10: History of Peace   Historical perspective on nonviolence and antiwar movements.   Small group activities to stimulate creative ideas for future peace.

Week 11: Connecting the Dots   Bringing all the previous concepts together in a perspective focused on unraveling the root causes of violence.

Peace Train became "The Bullet Train" and shot up to Seattle and Portland. Oliver and Tina e-mailed me that they altered the workshops making the first one a team building activity and the second one a group discussion on a topic deemed pertinent, such as "What do you see as the causes of violence in our society and what do you think can be done about it?" With Stef in San Francisco and Oakland, Oliver repeated the Seattle format, adding the question "What violent behavior is specific to your city and why?" In L.A. with Myriam the questions became "What role and responsibility does media have in societal violence?" and "Why is there gang violence?" They spent one day in San Diego where they added the question, "What do you think are the causes of sexual harassment in the military?" Dean flew back for two days to meet Oliver in Albuquerque, where there are large Native American and Hispanic populations. The discussions there centered on ways different cultures deal with violence. Ern went with him to three Texas cities, Dallas, San Antonio and Houston, and the key questions were "How effective do you think the death penalty is in deterring violence?" and " How does large scale immigration affect violence in a community?" When Peace Train went further south and east, Myriam hopped on to make two-day stops in New Orleans, Jackson, Birmingham, and Atlanta, where the questions were posed, "How far have we come since the Civil Rights Movement?" and "What role do you feel youth can play in bringing world peace?" as well as the general questions on violence.

Two K.C. staff co-facilitated with Oliver in Asheville, Nashville, Memphis, St. Louis, and stayed on through Peace Train's last stop, Chicago. Recalling his hometown as a very segregated city, Oliver asked the youth, "What is the role of poverty and classism in urban violence?" He decided to use "The Box" exercise again, noting the large number of multi-ethnic participants and the underlying tensions between youth from different neighborhoods.

When the trip was over Oliver sent an e-mail to all the regional staff, thanking them for their cooperation, diligent work, and resourceful spontaneity. His ending comments were, "It's inspiring to see how many young people are interested in pursuing a peaceful world. It makes me more convinced than ever that YPC must find a way to give every single one of them a chance at some point. On that note, Coordinators, please nobody call or e-mail me for a week. My engine has run out of steam, so I'm going to just sit on my caboose for awhile and chill."

Chapter 23

A group of us go to Ghana

Back in Miami I called ethnomusicologist cousin and told him we wanted to make a reconnaissance visit to his compound in Ghana. Six or seven staff were going to accompany me, and was there any chance he could meet us there. We'd buy the tickets for him and his wife and cover all expenses during our stay, hopefully a week. He checked his schedule and suggested Thanksgiving week; he'd ask for a few extra days off. Stacey, Oliver, Myriam, James, Tina, Ern and Cathy were the coordinators planning to go. Then I called Anthony in London, told him the dates and said YPC would pay for his whole family, wife and two kids, to join us there. "Perfect," he said.

Everybody checked their passports to make sure they hadn't expired and got the shots: yellow fewer, tetanus, hepatitis, and the maleria pills. Tina hand-carried everyone's paperwork to D.C. to form a personal relationship the Consulate and Embassy of Ghana, explaining that soon we might be requesting large quantities of visas, besides the eight we were then applying for. They were excited by the idea of our project and she found them very helpful. During her stay she also met with the U.S. Passport Service to work out a system for expediting our youth passports, or at least having someone as a personal contact to work out sticky situations, like youth who were having trouble acquiring birth certificates. YPC was going to supply the passports for any youth going abroad.

We arrived in Ghana on a Saturday afternoon, and were jet lagged until Sunday night. We spent that weekend in the compound, eating delicious local food prepared by ethnomusicologist cousin's cook, resting and looking around. We all stayed in the huts for the students, two per hut, with beds of foam mats on a wood frame, covered by mosquito netting. Eight huts were constructed in a circle. Student huts had no electricity and were illuminated by lanterns. Toilets and showers were in a separate location. The common spaces of the compound were a dining hall, which was a thatched roof cement-walled screened in building able to seat 20-25 people, and an open "rondaval," also with a thatched roof, that seated 10 or so and caught the ocean breezes coming in the front gate. The ocean was about 200 feet from the compound's entrance, but at that particular spot it had a powerful undertow, so we knew we needed to exercise great caution if the youth were going to swim there. There was also another rondaval which served as a classroom space, outside the front gates, not far from a broken down, tipped over fishing boat that the local children loved to play on. A short distance away was a schoolhouse which ethnomusiscologist's daughter and other students from her upstate New York college had constructed in one month, paid for by small foundation grants she had gotten.

We were trying to figure out a system to never have more than 25 youth in the compound at one time. Since we were going to be working in the surrounding areas, building wells and digging ditches for plumbing, we thought we could create "Tented Camps" where youth would live for three weeks at a time, then spend one week back at home base. Thus we could accommodate about 100 youth.

Ethnomusicologist cousin and his wife took us on tours in the "tro-tros," or vans which could carry 15 people, owned by the little transportation company they had formed. We agreed YPC would need to purchase 4 or 5 more vans to transport our group around, and we would hire local drivers. They introduced us to tribal chiefs, showed us some shrines and holy sites, took us to markets and villages, all the while experiencing the dirt roads, graveled if lucky, that were full of potholes, which in the rain grew to the size of small lakes. The weather was hot and the mosquitos were ferocious. Malaria and typhoid were common in those areas, and that's where Anthony came in.

Anthony's family, from the Ewe tribe, had a compound about half an hour away from my cousin's. I had met Anthony when he was 18 and studying in Lome, Togo to finish his baccalaureate exams. Subsequent to that he went to medical school in Germany and ended up in England, where he married and was finishing up his specialty studies. "You know, we need to build a clinic," he determined. "It could serve YPC and the local people. It wouldn't have to be too complex. A few examining rooms, a waiting room, and a pharmacy. What do you think?" We thought it sounded great. He committed to talking to some doctor friends to see if they would be interested in working with us, though it was still a ways away. We would pay them in American dollars, which we knew would be a strong incentive. One of the collective's first jobs would be to construct the clinic building. We could do it on a patch of land the community was willing to offer us.

Two days before we were ready to leave we went into Accra, the capital, three hours away. We had two meetings with government officials, informing them of the scope of our intended work, and going through the proper channels to function as a non-profit in Ghana. Through my cousin, we met professionals, professors and university students, mostly in the fields of engineering, architecture, and water technology. I told them YPC would pay any individual or group who designed a workable, environmentally safe, replicable system to bring running water to the whole of Ghana. The plans needed to contain drawings, methodology explanations, and locations where we could purchase the needed materials. Every group making a submission would be paid, and the group or individual whose idea was selected, would be hired by YPC to train youth and help oversee the project. We would return in April with some American professionals to select the winning plan, and also begin finding Ghanaian youth and staff to be part of the collective. We arranged for two friends of Anthony's to be local contacts, keeping close communication with headquarters office. They started out on an hourly wage, and in April were brought on full-time.

My head was spinning by the end of that trip, and all of us were itching like crazy. Hopefully no one would come down with malaria. Who had time?

Chapter 24

Tina Tells Aaron's Story
and
Mark adds to it

All during the trip to Ghana, Tina kept saying, "Aaron would have loved this." Yes, he was just the kind of kid who would have thrived in YPC. It is a tragedy that his life ended at age 20, and he missed so many experiences. After his death we thought of many projects we wanted to create for youth, in his memory. Somehow over time they all became intertwined with YPC. To tell his story is not easy, maybe too difficult to put down in words. But possibly getting it out will have a therapeutic effect, Tina thought, and help someone else.

Tina: There is nothing in life worse than losing a child. Ask any parent who has lost one. You never get over it, never. I think about Aaron every day, and though I know he's been gone five years and is in a better place, I still feel so deeply sad and hurt. Words can't even come close to describing it. He was my first child; I had him when I was 24. What a sweet little baby he was. I remember how he used to play with my mother; she'd feed him popcorn and the first pieces he would always put in her mouth. His short life was filled with so much death and tragedy though, it's weird, like he lived a whole lifetime of sorrow in the few years he was around. Maybe that's what gave him the underlying depression, desire to escape and buffer his pain, that led him to experiment with heroin. Somehow all his life I had this inexplicable feeling, like a premonition, that he wasn't going to live long. When he was 12 my father (his grandfather) dropped dead of a heart attack at Passover seder. Shortly after, one of my ex-boyfriends, who he had been close to, was killed in a boating accident, and then his uncle on his father's side committed suicide. A few years later, he was 15, his good friend was killed in a car accident driving back to school after going out for lunch. Aaron was in the car, and the seat his friend was in was where Aaron usually sat on the ride back to school. I guess he never stopped feeling that he should have been the one who died. A couple of years after that his grand-mother (my mom) passed away from lung cancer. That's a lot of loss for one kid to handle, especially a gentle and loving soul like Aaron. In the last weeks of his life he was painting the outside of my house, for extra money, besides being employed by his dad laying floors. He had gotten his GED, but wasn't interested in college, so he was sharing a small house with two friends and just working. That fateful night some "friend" supplied him and some buddies with heroin. I knew Aaron smoked pot and sometimes liked to do downers, but I really wasn't aware of the heroin thing. One of his roommates knew what they were going to do that night and decided not to hang around, and told him, "I'm not interested in being around that shit." They must have done heroin all night, because the next morning when that roommate got up to go to work, with Mark in fact and Aaron was supposed to go too, he saw Aaron lying in a weird position half off his bed. He left him there thinking, boy, these jerks really got themselves fucked up. Aaron was breathing, he said, in a kind of congested way. Life is very strange. I needed to see Aaron that day and was going to stop by in the morning, but instead ran around doing some errands and planned to see him in the afternoon. Mark, even though he expected him at work, didn't call or go by to see what had happened. Any of us might have intervened, but we didn't. That's when I came to believe that when it's your time, it's your time. In the middle of the afternoon I got a page from Mark with "911" on it, coming from Aaron's phone number. At that moment I knew something terrible had happened. Just the week before I had gotten mad at Aaron for paging me with "911" to ask if I wanted to buy a concert ticket. I told him only to use it in a real emergency, because he had scared me. Oh God. Mark had gotten to the house and found Aaron dead. Ultimately we were told it was from an infection around his heart, but later I learned that sort of thing happens from dirty needles. For anyone reading this, I pray you never have to go through the loss of a child. There is nothing, absolutely nothing, more horrible on earth.

Mark: What the fuck can I say? I've been through a helleva lot of shit in my life, but losing Aaron was the worst. Maybe I was a fucked up dad. Maybe I failed him, yeah, that might be it. But damn, I loved that sweet kid and I still do. Tina pretty much told you how it came down, so I won't repeat the details. But I guess I want to say, our children are a treasure; we need to appreciate and protect them the best we can, while we can. I'll never understand how a parent can fucking encourage their kid to join the military and put themselves in the line of fire. Cause dead is dead, no matter what the reasons, ideals or circumstances. They're fucking gone and will never be back again. That's heavy, man. It's final, the end, period. Life itself is dangerous; I know that better than most people. But to send a kid to kill folks for some hairbrained scheme of a president, no fucking way. And then your own child gets killed, no man, it's not right. If I had Aaron with me right now I'd give him the biggest hug and tell him a million times, "I love you, kid." But unfortunately, I'm not so lucky. When I heard about YPC I said, "Count me in, for all the Aarons of the world."

Chapter 25

INS, IRS, CBS

You don't want to know how many days I spent at the Immigration and Naturalization Service office at Biscayne and 79th in Miami trying to get work visas for Anthony, Florence, Tate and Thabisile. Standing in long lines outside the building, shuffled from one office to another, forms to fill out and get notarized, documentation to present, fees to pay. What a hassle, but I managed it. They were all coming over to join us for a meeting in Kansas City in March. Florence would come to live in Miami and focus on organizing inquiries and applications at the headquarters office. Tate and Thabs, both of whom I met in Durban, South Africa in 1996, would be "coordinators" and start out spending three months in K.C., then go to summer training. Anthony was coming as a consultant, to meet the kids, give some lectures about health conditions and risks in Africa, and educate the collective about the culture and customs of Ghana.

This tidbit might astonish you; the people working at IRS are really nice. After ten or twelve phone calls where friendly phone voices transferred me to different departments because of the unusual nature of my question, I finally reached the appropriate person to help me figure out how YPC could pay the youth $10,000 without taxes. We had one meeting in Washington, D.C. and I hardly understood the details, but Jeffrey and our accountant did, and that's all that matters to me. It had to do with the organization paying a bulk tax for all the youth, or something like that. In any case, the taxes on income would be paid, but not out of the youth's money.

Then CBS called and wanted to do a special on YPC. They had seen a few articles written about us in New York and Miami newspapers and had read an account of summer training, in People magazine when three YPC youth were profiled. I called the folks in K.C. and told them about the offer. It required the youth to agree to be filmed and interviewed while they worked at The Lanes, were renovating the offices, and allowing the cameras into their apartments at Cooperation House. The response I got was one word: NO! Cathy said the youth collective wanted me to know that they were planning a video project and would film, interview and narrate themselves, and then "see if CBS wants to buy it from us." That was that.

Chapter 26

When do I get to go to Africa?

The most frequent question the kids asked me when I went to K.C. in March was, "When do I get to go to Africa?" I explained that we were hoping to start that next September, but it had not been completely finalized. We could only take 25 youth per month, until we had worked out the "tented camp" situation. In the meantime they had four new African staff to barrage with questions. This first group of YPC youth was just finishing up their six-month stint (they had been given two weeks off at Christmas and New Years). The Lanes was already in operation, but the Art Cafe had not even begun construction. The offices had been tackled first, and they were nearly finished. "Anyone who wants to take a break, can," I told them. "We'll keep in touch with you and you can apply for Africa over the summer." Tina and Jeffrey were working on setting up bank accounts for all the kids in their home cities, where we were going to deposit their $10,000. During their six months they had been receiving $50 in cash every Friday after work as "weekend spending money."

The Coordinators were busy hiring more staff and finishing the selection of youth for the upcoming summer training. Our goal was to have all 50 states represented in youth participants and have a second model project ready to start after training. We decided that no youth would be allowed to go abroad without working at least six months on a project inside the U.S. Miami was the logical next spot to set up urban projects; the boys had already agreed to rent us the entire Tower Hotel. It would function as a temporary Cooperation House, while the youth were renovating a square block of boarded up former housing project units in Liberty City, which we were going to call "Cooperation City." Two of the units would be converted into "Peace and Books," a small cafe and used book store, with its initial stock of books provided by my bookseller-on-the-street cousin in New York. Also, we found a site in "Little Haiti" to build The Lanes from the ground up. A "bowling alley" cousin, who has worked over 20 years in a bowling center in Columbia, Maryland, offered to help as a consultant, volunteering her husband, a carpenter, as well. YPC gave them a one-week all expense paid "vacation" at the scenic Tower Hotel, while they helped us review and revise architectural plans. In Miami there would be enough work for hundreds of kids. El alcalde (the Mayor) was helpful in opening doors for us to acquire the abandoned Liberty City real estate, as well as a plot of land off NE Second Avenue, and for that we are eternally grateful.

Sixty-four of the 92 youth, one got sick and had to leave in the middle of the term, signed up for the next six months. They wanted to continue working on the Cafe project and see it to completion, then open the Cafe and run it. Some of the kids asked if they could work with the architect and help design the interior because they had ideas for a daycare area and what they called "the poetry corner." By this time The Lanes Northeast, that's how we referred to it, was accommodating bowling leagues four evenings a week, disco bowl on Friday and Saturday nights, and offering "Super Sunday" where a line cost only 50 cents from 10 a.m. - 2 p.m. If you walked in there you might see a 6'2" hulking youth bending over and showing a six year old how to throw the ball. It was very touching. And they even served good food. The tiny kitchen offered one soup (different every day) and three sandwich selections. Not a huge variety, but tasty.

During my visit, I was able to catch a performance of "Harpeace." Fourteen youth had been studying harp with my friend Roseanne, an accomplished harpist, choosing that instrument for its soothing qualities and peaceful sound. Their intention was to offer music at nursing homes, hospitals, schools, and any religious institutions. Roseanne was teaching them "Take Me Out to the Ballgame," "Twinkle, Twinkle Little Star" and other favorites like "Amazing Grace." I heard them play at former Mayor Emanuel Cleaver II's church, where the entire group joined him in a powerful rendition of "Silent Night."

I held various all-group discussions with the YPC members in K.C. We talked about our goals for the upcoming years, suggestions the kids had for changes in the training for the next summer group, comments on some "nearly violent" behavior they were observing related to some "couples," and they expressed a desire to have youth from other countries working with them in the States. They also talked about feeling depressed, reading the news and realizing that even though they were all engaged in the work of peace, the world still had war in many places, and nothing seemed to change that.

I reminded the group about the theory of the "Hundred Monkeys." Nobody seems to know exactly where this theory came from or if it's really true, but I choose to believe it, and that's what I told the kids. It basically goes something like this. At one time in the world all the monkeys on every continent peeled their bananas in a certain way. That's how their species did it. But suddenly, for no explicable reason, a group of monkeys, let's say in Central America somewhere, began peeling their bananas differently. One by one the monkeys in that vicinity began emulating the new method and when 100 monkeys had incorporated the new peeling method into their habitual pattern, miraculously, without any way of long-distance communication (they had no fax, phones or e-mail) monkeys in continents thousands of miles away began peeling in the new fashion. It was a type of "collective unconscious" that exists in species, a way that actions of one sector of the species affect other sectors. I told them we were like the monkeys, but the thing we were going to change was how human beings live with one another on earth. We were initiating the way of "peaceful and respectful cooperation," which we hoped would replace the former way, of disrespectful and violent domination. I said that just now 100 of us were consciously beginning this process, and that we'd have to wait for the addition of the next group of youth in training and the Ghanaian youth who were going to start with us in the fall to start turning the tide. Then, watch out, the Youth Peace Collective was going to stimulate peace in every corner of the globe.

Two incidents occurred while I was visiting, which let me know what the youth were referring to in their comments about "couples." At The Lanes one day, Thomas and Mimi were both working, she behind the counter and he on lane maintenance. They have been a "couple" (on and off to be sure, and not infrequently belligerent in the Streetwork days) for over 4 years. Mimi saw Thomas "chatting up" one of the girls who was bowling on Lane 2. They were laughing and flirting; I was watching it from a bar stool in the Cafe. When she could tolerate it no longer, because she watched, fuming, for a long time, she went up to him and barked, "Okay motherfucker, get back to work." Greatly humiliated in front of his potential conquest, he replied, "Shut the fuck up, bitch and get out of my face." Mimi raised her hand as if to slap him, and at that moment Carmen, the other youth working the counter yelled, "POW WOW!" I ran over, along with two other staff and three youth collective members. Mimi was screaming, "You God Damn Motherfucker. You always do this to me. I hate you, you asshole." Thomas screamed back, "I'm sick of you, cunt. Get out of my life. I never want to see you again. I can't put up with your fucking shit anymore." Carmen grabbed Mimi and said, "Come with me." Enrique, the daytime Manager of The Lanes, told Thomas the same thing, and took him into his office. The disputants were counseled in separate corners for about 20 minutes, and then Enrique brought them together and said, "You are both suspended from work today. You are to go see Lyla (a psychologist/therapist "on call" for YPC) at 4:00 p.m. today for couple's counseling. You will see Lyla three times a week for the next four weeks and the issue will be brought to Collective Council to determine if there will be other consequences. Is that agreed?" They looked at each other menacingly, but agreed and walked out, Mimi saying to Thomas, "Give me a cigarette, asshole."

The other incident occurred when I was at Cooperation House, talking to two roommates in their apartment one evening. A frantic knock was heard at their door, and someone calling, "Janet! Janet! Quick, come out!" I rushed out and Tyrell said, "Come right now. There's a mess happening in 208." We ran down the hall and as I arrived I heard, "Maricon!!!!!! Get out of here! Faggot! What do you think you're doing fucking in my apartment?!" I said to Tyrell, "Go get Bernard (the nighttime manager) now! And knock on some doors and say pow wow in 208." Lorenzo had walked into his apartment and found his roommate Jacob and another boy, Rene (also called Renata, because he sometimes cross dressed) with their shirts off, kissing. "Chinga tu madre, pinche marica hijo de puta,...." (can't translate that friends, ask a Mexican) Lorenzo was yelling, as the two boys were putting on their shirts and Jacob was softy saying, "We were just kissing." I stepped in the room and said sternly, "Lorenzo, cálmate y cállate, YA!." (calm down and be quiet, right now) "Tell me what happened." Lorenzo explained, "I was downstairs in the music room and it was getting cold so I came up to get a sweatshirt and when I walked in these two maricones were here in my apartment fucking. That's disrespectful." "Lorenzo, they were not fucking," I corrected, "They have their clothes on. They were kissing." "Whatever. I'm not sharing a room with a queer." "Lorenzo," I posed "what would you have thought if you walked in on Jacob kissing a girl?" He grinned, "I would have thought, hey, the dude is scoring." Me: "Well, the dude was scoring. It's only your prejudice that is turning this into a negative thing. One issue is disrespect, of someone engaging in romantic activity in your shared room....." As I was saying this Bernard ran into the room. "What's going on?" he asked, out of breath. We told him and he rolled his eyes. "Janet, it's time for another workshop about homophobia, and I think we need a few on appropriate sexual conduct in the apartments. This is the third time I've had to deal with this in the last two weeks, people walking in on people doing whatever, and one time it was a guy's girlfriend doing it with another girl. That was really fun." "Yeah," one of the kids who responded to the pow wow call chimed in, "Why can't YPC rent us some hotel rooms somewhere, or at least give us vouchers or something?" "This requires some thought and discussion," I stated. "We'll call a community-wide meeting soon. Now you three go with Bernard and get this worked out. And Lorenzo, no more name calling, mihijo."

Amma Mama came to K.C. for one week. The kids were thrilled and she was kept busy "Amma"ing. She only got to drop one bad joke, which she did at The Lanes one Sunday morning when she was bowling, and two 7 year olds next to her started an argument over a bowling ball. In the midst of their grabbing the ball away from each other she said, "Hey, do you guys know what's the difference between roast chicken and pea soup?" They stopped and shook their heads. "Anybody can roast chicken." That kept them thinking.

The regions were feeling completely overwhelmed with the interest in YPC. Everyone had been telling me that the number of applications coming in was far exceeding our most optimistic projections. So many kids wanted to join, more than we could ever afford. What were we going to do?

I knew it was time to start putting my fundraising idea in motion. For reasons which you will understand later, we didn't carry it out until the middle of September, but I'm going to tell you about it now.

Chapter 27

Share 1
Each ONE Makes a Difference

The Share 1 fundraising idea came to me that prolific summer of 2000. Initially I wanted to use it to ask owners of multiple apartment buildings in New York City to "Share 1" apartment for "homeless" youth. I was going to ask companies to "Share 1" job. There was also a money-raising component. My dream was for it to benefit Streetwork youth who, in conjunction with staff, were going to carry out the campaign. Michael, at that time the receptionist of Streetwork, called his friend Gil, a graphic designer, who kindly (without pay) allowed me to describe my logo idea over the phone and he tried to put it on paper. I never met Gil, but he gave us four drafts. This one felt the closest to my idea.

The campaign was never a realistic possibility for Streetwork, and in the midst of a multitude of shelter details, I totally forgot about it. I had "shared" the idea with Partnership for the Homeless, but it wasn't workable for them either.

When the time was ripe, I pulled Share 1 out of the old shoulder bag, dusted off the cobwebs, and adjusted it for YPC. Jeni completely reworked the concept.

The intention was to have the concept of "sharing" become more dominant in our cultural lexicon. The tag line, Each ONE makes a difference, was to stress the notion that for every ONE you shared, ONE was helped. The Youth Peace Collective used Share 1

strictly as a fund-generating activity, to invite everyone in the country to support a project that could ultimately benefit their children and the world. It gave people who wanted to encourage "peace in action" a place to put their dollars.

We didn't initiate Share 1 until the second week of September, because I needed all the youth who had been in summer training to participate. Here's what we did. First I called a lifelong friend, Sheena's uncle, who has been an advertising executive in New York City for 30 years. He agreed to work with me on an "ad" which would run for 45 seconds, at primetime, for one week. The creation of the promotional spot would be easy, and an anonymous donor, a very well known television personality, had agreed to pay for the network time, no small sum. We established one main contact group working with "at risk" youth in the largest city of every one of the fifty states. Some states, like California, had three contact agencies: in L.A., San Francisco and San Diego. The campaign would run for one week only. Starting on Monday of that week the ads would appear on TV and we would have a full page newspaper spread in the principal paper of each big city on Monday and Wednesday. The newspaper text, beneath our logo, would read:

> The Youth Peace Collective invites everyone in America to Share 1 for youth and for peace in the world.
>
> The Youth Peace Collectives works with 18-25 year olds building water infrastructure in de-

veloping nations and creating urban youth-run projects in the United States.

Youth participants live and work collectively, learn and practice the principles of peace, receive practical and theoretical training, make decisions by consensus, and are fairly compensated.

SHARE $1, 10, 100, 1,000 Checks and cash are accepted. If you own more than 5 homes, share $1,000,000.

On the second Friday of September in [name of city] Youth Peace Collective members will be accepting donations at [locations where the youth will be stationed].

You may also mail donations to:
Youth Peace Collective
Post Office Box 350925
Miami, Florida 33135

Join us in ending war and bringing peace to our earth. Share 1. Each ONE makes a difference.

The youth at summer training had created 200 five foot number 1's, each individual making his/her own unique "one." They had constructed the number one, three dimensional, out of cardboard, such that it could be filled with checks and money. It had a slot somewhere in the top and a way to open it on the bottom. The outside form of all boxes was the same, but each "one" was a spectacular work of art, in its own right.

After the campaign was over, each "one" was auctioned off (like the cows in New York and the flamingos in Miami), the bidding price starting at the amount of money that was collected in that particular box.

Each youth-serving agency committed to staffing the donation collection from 7 a.m. to 7 p.m. on that Friday. At least one Youth Peace Collective member would be at each location, and all the individuals working would be wearing YPC t-shirts (the color for year two was yellow). All youth and staff manning the collection boxes would be paid $10/hour in cash at the end of the day. We had arranged money pick-ups and bank drop-offs, people to keep running accounts and tabulations, and we were going to hold a press conference at twelve noon the next day to announce the total we had collected. It was a resounding success! The boxes all over America brought in a little over $12 million in one day. Auctions gave us about another $14 million and individual contributions sent to the P.O. box totalled just under $8 million. $34 million, and that's not including the cost of paying the workers, because we paid them on the very day of the campaign and did not include it in the amounts we announced at the press conference.

Our TV ad was clear and simple. Each shot was a full face frontal of a Youth Peace Collective member or staff, one at a time, reciting a line. The logo came on first, then:

Gail: The Youth Peace Collective is constructing peace in the world.

Carlitos: We are bringing clean water to developing nations.
Mimi: We have created The Lanes, a youth-run bowling alley.
Chen Li: And Cooperation House, transitional and long term housing.
Thomas: We live and work collectively.
Tina: And make decisions by consensus.
Mohammed: We treat one another with respect and fairness.
Katarina: Believing in and living by The Golden Rule.
Laquisha: Share 1 with us; share our vision.
Reynolds: Each one helps; each one is helped.
James: This Friday Share 1 boxes will be in all the 50 states.
Tomoko: Open your hearts and your wallets.
Running Red Deer: Join us in making war obsolete.
Ernie: Share 1, Each ONE makes a difference.

Then the screen flashed: Donations in check or cash can be sent to: YPC
Box 350925
Miami, FL 33135

Thank the spirit of the universe, every state had beautiful weather that Friday. The kids and staff had a ball at the collection spots, talking with people and handing out our brochures. The only minor mishap was when one box in Salt Lake City, Utah was drenched by a donor accidentally spilling his entire cup of coffee on it. The box creator agreed to repair it, if she could, or make a new one for the auction.

For each $1,000 donated, an individual would receive a set of five multi-colored posters with original artwork by Joanne Schiller, an artist friend of mine in Miami. Here are the posters:

"The Struggle"

"Romance in the 60's"

"Afro-American 1990"

"Red, Black and Blue"

"Forgotten Promises"

We intended to hold the Share 1 campaign for one week in September every year. We would use the money brought in by different regions to start projects in that part of the country, and a certain portion of the funds would be for overseas programs. Any donor could sign up to receive our quarterly newsletters, updating them on our activities. We never wanted to badger people with funding appeals or materials they had not solicited. That first campaign was covered quite extensively by the media. They even helped us make our "Grand Announcement" a major media event. On Saturday at noon, the day after Share 1 Friday, Oliver and Gail stood outside the entrance to the United Nations in New York, cameras zooming in on them. Oliver said, "We want to announce the results of Share 1, the Youth Peace Collective's nation-wide fundraiser. The envelope please." Thomas walked up and handed them an envelope. Gail opened it, and in an excited voice yelled, "Total from the boxes: TWELVE MILLION, ONE HUNDRED TWENTY EIGHT THOUSAND, SIX HUNDRED FIFTY FIVE DOLLARS!!!!!!!!!" The crowd, YPC members and supporters, cheered. All the cameras caught a great shot of Oliver, Thomas and Gail in the three-way hug, which showed up on the front page, at least of the New York papers and the Kansas City Star. Every local news station carried a clip of it on the six o'clock news, with the soundbite "$12,128,655 dollars!!!!!!!!"

Special thanks are appropriate here for the 100+ postal workers at the Jose Marti Station in Miami, Florida. Before the campaign began I had rented in YPC's name three additional large post office boxes, because our original one was on the small side. I assumed that would cover the quantity of mail we would receive. Wrong. The letters came in in such volume, that the mailroom distributors started leaving them in canvas bags and letting us take them like that. One counter clerk asked me, "Hey girlfriend, what are you giving away for free?" A supervisor said, "Carajo, chica. Jamás he visto una cosa semejante." ([untranslatable] girl, I've never seen anything like this.) On Friday the week after Share 1, we brought 30 large pizzas and 30 liters of soda to the post office for lunch, as a small token of our gratitude for their work in processing the mail. In my mind, I was already scheming a Christmas gift I would bring for the station, maybe $20 gift certificates to the movies for the whole crew, or something like that.

Share 1 supported us from here on out, with the addition of a few unthinkably generous gifts, which you will hear about in due time. The auctions were always held in New York, and every year our collection boxes were a different structure – like big bowling balls made out of paper mache, cardboard apartment buildings, and replicas of wells, made from heavy carton packing containers in the shape of big garbage cans. You get the idea.

Chapter 28

Ghana Welcomes Us

In April Stacey, Oliver, James, Mark and Gail had returned to Ghana and spent nearly a month, selecting youth and staff for the project, hiring local residents as work crew leaders, and setting up things to prepare for construction of the clinic. Ernie and I flew over for one week, along with six professionals in the fields of engineering and water technology. The submissions were varied and interesting, though I didn't completely grasp all the technical theories. Even those who didn't win were pleased, because we gave $1,500 U.S. dollars to every group (to be divided among the collaborators) or individual who submitted a serious proposal. The winning group comprised of one professional and two university students, received $5,000 and proposed a system that used gas generators and well water. YPC would dig wells and then construct raised platforms for large tanks of water that would be pumped out of the wells by the generators. Gravity brought the water down from the tanks and it could be channeled to shower spigots or toilets. YPC would dig the ditches for thick tubing which was designed for proper disposal of sewage waters. The plan proposed creating a "Shower House" and "Toilet House" in each village, as well as a location with four taps for drawing water for cooking, clothes washing, etc. Each village would work with YPC to determine where they wanted the facilities located and how many of each they needed.

Clean water was so essential. Most residents in the countryside used outhouses. Communal wells were easily contaminated when they were shared by large numbers of people, and the run-off water often became a breeding ground for malaria-carrying mosquitos. Anybody not washing their hands after going to the bathroom, could infect an entire well with typhoid. Ernie contacted companies making the generators, tubing, shower parts and toilets and began negotiating contracts for large-scale purchases. Local laborers were hired to create some model projects and build 8 more student huts that would be completed before the American youth arrived in late September. They were thrilled to know we wanted them to initially help us in our "tented camps," as we starting spreading the project to the countryside. YPC made a dent in the unemployment rate, which was quite high, of the Volta region.

The mothers of the youth selected for YPC were all giggly and chattering the day they came to sign up for the project, along with their sons and daughters. In order to "spread the wealth" we stated that no family (people living together in one house) could have more than one child in YPC at any given time and that no youth could work for more than one six-month stint. It was explained to everyone that the first week of September would be a one week training for all 60 youth selected and that as the American youth began arriving in late September the Ghanaian youth would join progressively in groups of 15. The coordinators held three days of workshops explaining the concepts of collectivity and peace education, demonstrating some group dynamic exercises, and instructing them in how the work crews would operate. The youth and their mothers (grandmothers, sisters, Aunts, or whoever had raised them) each received the equivalent of $30 in local currency for successful completion of the three days. They would be given double that amount for training in early September, and at the end of their six-month stint, they would be paid the equivalent of $450. That was nearly double what an average Ghanaian makes in a year, if they have a job. Ghana's local currency is the CEDI, which means cowry shell in an ancient language. $1 = 8000 CEDI. The minimum daily wage was 9000 CEDI/day, which is a little over one dollar. The youth collective member would end up with a significant amount of money for six months' work, and so would the family. During the six-month stint, each American and Ghanaian youth would receive 20,000 CEDI (approximately $2.50) every Friday evening as "weekend spending money."

The first group of 25 American kids, with ten staff, came over the last week of September. I was there to greet them and watch their faces as they entered the compound, after traveling on the bumpy roads from the airport in Accra. Comments were flying around like, "Unbelievable; I'm in Africa," "We didn't see any giraffe and zebra. Where are they?" and "Shit, it's hot!" Fifteen of the Ghanaian youth were in the compound to show the American kids to their huts and help them get settled. Everyone was told that after dinner there would be a Welcoming Ceremony. They rested then ate in the dining area, where I noticed Thomas looking strangely at some of the items on his plate. I went up to him and whispered, "Remember you said you'd *try* to eat African food." He smiled wanly.

That night the Chief whose tribe had owned the lands bought by ethnomusicologist cousin gave a welcoming speech, translated by Razaki, one of our Ghanaian staff, and he performed a blessing ceremony to ensure the health of all participants, to consecrate the work we were about to do to benefit all the people of Ghana, and thanking the ancestors. Three drummers performed, and the local mothers danced some of their traditional dances. Twenty or thirty little local children wandered in and out, and sat on the ground watching or playing with some of the American girls' hair.

I offered brief comments, thanking the tribal Chief, all the residents of the region who had been so helpful from the first moment we arrived there, and blessing all the youth for the work they were beginning in the name of peace.

That night we held a "Song Fest." Every individual or group that felt motivated, sang a song for everyone else. African harmonies, a few rap numbers, some of the old folk songs like "If I had a Hammer" and "Michael, row your boat ashore, a couple tunes in Spanish like Flor de la Canela and the more modern "Vive la Vida Loca," and numerous current pop and rock songs filled the air that night, as the Youth Peace Collective began its work abroad.

The Ghanaian youth showed the Americans how to get into their beds and arrange the mosquito netting for most effective results. I'm not sure they all got the trick, because as I wandered through the compound in the wee hours I would frequently hear a SLAP and then a "Damn!"

The rest of the first week was run like summer training, small-group workshops in the morning and all-group infrastructure building lectures/instruction in the afternoon. We established that our work hours would be from 8 a.m. to noon and then 2-5 p.m., four days a week. Fridays would still be all-day theoretical trainings, plus art and musical activities, and weekends would be free.

In general the American kids were enjoying the food. There were large quantities of fresh fruit – pineapple, watermelon, oranges, bananas, and mangos. Many dishes were spicy, like "hot pepe stew" with red peppers in it. The meats were often ram, goat or chicken. Being so close to the ocean, we bought fabulous fresh fish from the local fishermen, and there were unlimited amounts of rice, as well as fufu and "akple," which is a fermented mixture of cassava and maize, a doughy substance. I describe fufu, which is made from cassava as well, as having the consistency of slightly hard mashed potatoes. You pull off a piece of it and dip it into sauce, at the same time picking up a small piece of whatever meat is in the sauce. For snacks, there was always fresh coconut, since the trees grew inside the compound and the children loved scampering up and throwing them down. Some of the American kids, such as Mimi and Katarina who loved to cook, convinced the compound cooks to let them prepare a few meals for the group. Katarina made "chile relleno" (green peppers stuffed with ground beef – a treat) and Mimi made hamburgers and "french fries" and a type of chicken parmigiana.

The two African cooks and their three helpers, all women, started a very funny ritual. Every afternoon at 5 p.m. as the youth wearily filed into the compound, they would sing a certain song and make some bird-calling noises. They would kind of dance around the kids as they came in, and teasingly poke some of them in the ribs. Kufi, a Ghanaian youth explained that it was a humorous song the women had invented, as if they were greeting their warriors returning from far off lands. They did it because they had so much affection for the kids.

After orientation the kids spent a solid week digging. Some were digging wells, others deep rows for the sewage piping, and many were preparing the ground for the walls of the clinic. How their backs ached. That's when Amma Mama arrived. "You're a sight for sore shoulders," James told her as he gave her a hug. Along with Deb, came my friend Nancy, her 8 year old daughter Sonia, and my youngest brother, but I'll explain about them in a moment. The four of them were staying only two weeks.

Amma Mama was a given a hut all her own, which the kids named and even made a sign for: "Massage Parlor." Equipped with only her chair, Deb had her hands full (pun intended). Even when she was hanging out in the rondaval, on her off time, somebody might say, "Hey Mama, could you just rub my shoulder a little bit right here?" Many of the youth were asking her questions about what Amma meant, how was she able to move their energy around, or why they felt like crying when she touched certain points in their bodies. So we picked a night and Deb gave us a talk on Amma, in the classroom outside the compound. All the little local kids were there and chanting "Amma. Mama. Amma. Mama...." The kitchen ladies were there too, because they were fascinated by this new resident that everybody was pulling one direction or another.

Here is what Amma Mama told us.

Amma is a story that was told to me, that I tell each time with you, saying it's okay, being here, being human, on this earth at this time. Every thing is all right. We might not know where we're going, but we're on our way. It's like stillness in motion. Like I build a little house around you, and when I leave, you still have the house. You're my garden. I'm the gardener.

"Amma" means to bring peace with the hands. It's a Japanese form of acupressure that is over 1300 years old. Hey, you know Helen Keller, that blind lady, well, she saved Amma. It used to be the profession of blind people in Japan, but after World War II when General McArthur was running things, he saw some people doing Amma and he decided it was witchcraft and had it declared illegal. Some blind people organizations called Helen Keller and she went to the president of the United States and convinced him to make it legal again.

Amma reassures you, "You can do it." That's what my teacher Scott whispered to me one day when I was doubting myself, and I'll never forget it. "You can do it." I've been doing Amma for 12 or 14 years and it energizes me as much as it energizes you. It activates my points when I activate yours. When I ask do you want a message I feel like I'm asking, "Do you want to go dancing?" It's a way I get to use my thumbs, palms, elbows, fists, and forearm to say "Welcome to the world" to your body. To tell you, you're not just in your head. You're bigger than you think you are.

One person I messaged said "Some of what you did to me was silly." Maybe they were talking about "yo-kode" that feels like a bird, or "shukendaho," the thundering fists from heaven. Amma is comforting, like a beautiful song. We share breath together. When I hold your head I have a little prayer inside me, "May this head find peace," and for your hands, "May they do good things." When I slowly bring down your leg and you can't even feel where it is, I think of the stars and like the spaceship Enterprise out there in the galaxies.

I add humor to Amma too, like when I spread a sheet over somebody who was cold I said, "Sheet on you." Amma is always done through clothing, on a table or a chair. My table's name is Eunice, which is Greek for great victory. The first time I lay down on her (she's blue) I said to myself, "You nice-a table." My chair (also blue) is named Myrna Loy Murn, after Myrna Loy who is small and powerful (so I get to say "Murnamurn!," one of my favorite exclamations – it means rejoice). In San Francisco I always do my first massage for free and then I have a sliding scale from zero to a bazillion. My feeling is if you're going to trust me to massage you, I'm going to trust you to pay me what you can afford. One woman back home stopped biting her nails after getting Amma. After the message, I always make a pot of tea and sit and talk for as long as people want. Most everybody likes to talk about life and the universe and stuff like that. Sometimes I mention my favorite philosopher, Lao Tzu, he's Chinese from 300 B.C., I'm taking old. One of his most encouraging sayings is, "No matter how great you pretend to be, it is not as great as you truly are." Doing Amma is an honor for me. In fact, I wish I could Amma the whole world.

So since I'm the official Amma Mama of YPC, I want everybody to come up and pick out a mandala. I painted them, every one is different, and they release the forces of goodness for all living beings. And ya know, I'm still going to tell bad jokes whenever I can.

The listeners came up and got their mandalas and Deb sat around talking to a group of kids for many more hours.

I had asked Nancy to come over to help with our first expedition into Togo to find youth to join YPC. I had planned a 5 day trip to Lome and nearby areas, and wanted her to be part of the group going, which included Stacey, Gail, Oliver, and Kwame and Adzo, two of our Ghanaian staff. Togo's colonial language is French (Ghana's is English) and Nancy had lived twenty years in France. I also wanted her along because I trusted her perceptive eye and she was a technical writer. She had taken the part-time job of producing our Annual Reports. Little Sonia stayed in the compound while we traveled and collective members helped take care of her, with the kitchen ladies trying to keep her within shouting distance as best they could. In Lome we met students from some baccelaureate schools and one university, and with one social service agency. We drove around the countryside to see if their water situation was similar to Ghana's; it was. The Togolese youth expressed great interest in joining YPC, but the language issue posed a complication.

My youngest brother (the one on whose fire escape this whole thing started) was there as a videographer. Along with our Annual Report we were going to produce a 20 minute video of the year's activities. He spent the two weeks filming our projects there, plus getting comments on tape from youth, staff, the cooks, families of YPC members and local residents. His footage would be added to the video the youth in K.C. had produced, along with some shots of our renovations at Antioch, and our next sites in Miami. He had equipment in his apartment in New York to edit it..

The day after we got back to the compound, the second group of 25 American youth and 15 Ghanaian were coming in. The first group of youth had all gone to a "tented camp" which they set up 50 miles from us. Ernie had purchased some outdated army tents, which were still in good shape and could sleep 4 people. They set up a tent for "sickbay" and an extra large one for "meetings." In their camp they built a "dining room" made of four poles on the sides, four poles across the top, and a huge plastic tarp thrown over the top and sealed down some how. Cooking was done outside, and they had one Ghanaian cook with youth collective helpers. There were four villages surrounding their camp, and they intended bringing wells, showers and toilets to them all. When the first village's toilet/well/shower facilities had been completed I got a call that said I had to come out to that village right away. The tribal chief of that area was going to do a ceremony blessing the communal grounds, and he asked to meet the little lady with wild hair who was giving away so much money. The chief, a man about my age, poured libations (a mixture of water, a certain type of alcohol and a traditional drink like maize and water) and said prayers thanking the ancestors. There was singing and traditional drumming. After the ceremony, when the chief walked away, some of the village woman motioned to me that they wanted me to flush a toilet. As we heard the flush, gurgle of the water, all the women started laughing and began making a shrill sound, which turned into singing and chanting. I felt like I was missing a joke.

I had been more than two months in Ghana, and needed to return to New York City for a very important meeting. Before I left I got a call from Nancy back in the States, wanting to tell me something interesting Sonia had said after her stay at the compound. Sonia, by the way, is an utterly amazing child. Her father is Algerian, her mother American Jewish, and she lived the first five years of her life in France. She is quick-witted, smart as a whip and self-confident. In fact, Sonia "reads souls." At one point she began informing her mother who was a young soul and who was an old soul. Sometimes she would say, about the babysitter for example, "Oh mom, it's a shame she's such a young soul," and she pronounced my graphic designer cousin a " very VERY old soul." Unfortunately I asked her to read so many peoples souls that she protested, "I'm going to charge you $10 per soul." Sonia's comment, that Nancy wanted me to hear, was "Mom, you know all those kids in Africa who are making toilets and bringing peace, well, I'm going to be like them when I grow up, only I'm going to bring washing machines to the women so they don't have to scrunch down and scrub their clothes and the little kids don't have to carry buckets of water on their heads. And mom, I think maybe one day I'll be the solver of all the world's problems." Maybe she will.

At noontime the day I left for the Accra airport, I was walking through the compound with my suitcase when I caught a glimpse of Thomas in the dining room. He called out, "Hey Janet. Have a safe trip, and you know, I fucking love this fufu shit."

Chapter 29

I win over the Mayor of New York with Mandel Bread

Manhattan foundation cousin had performed a wonderful deed – arranged a meeting for me with the Mayor of New York City. When I arrived at her apartment the night before, I said, "I may be up all night because there's something I absolutely must do before I meet him tomorrow." "What's that?" she inquired. "Bake Mandel Bread."

For some reason I thought, as a nice Jewish boy, he might really love Mandel Bread. I needed anything I could find to help me with the huge favor I was about to ask of him. My Mandel Bread, actually my mother's, which is really my Aunt Dorothy's (of blessed memory) recipe, is often proclaimed "the best I've ever eaten" by people who try it. I had to give it a shot.

Mandel Bread, a biscuit type cookie, is usually a two-day procedure, but I didn't have that luxury. You make the batter one day, with common ingredients that my cousin had on hand, except pecans which I found at a 24-hour store, and let it sit in the refrigerator overnight. In a rush, it can sit for 2-3 hours in the fridge before using, which is what I had to do. Then you knead a fourth of the dough in flour and roll out (on a cutting board, with your hands) four logs and place them on greased cookie sheets, bake for thirty minutes, then cut them up in half-inch slices, lay them flat, sprinkle a cinnamon and sugar mixture on the "up" side and bake them for 8 minutes, then turn them over and put the sugar mixture on the other side and bake for another 8 minutes. It's not as complicated as people think, but you kind of burn your fingers flipping the hot slices. At 3:00 a.m. the batch was done and perfect.

The next morning at 10:30 a.m. I was led into the Mayor's office downtown. "Good morning," he shook my hand. "Please sit down." I sat down and then stood back up and said, "I brought these for you. They're my homemade Mandel Bread, my Aunt Dorothy's recipe." "Mandel Bread!" he said, with his eyes lighting up. "I LOVE Mandel Bread!!" He buzzed his assistant, "Two coffees in here, please, when you can. How do you like yours? (to me) Milk and sugar? (I nodded) Two regulars." When he tasted the Mandel Bread, he leaned back in his chair and pronouned, "Best I've ever eaten."

"Now, what can I do for you? Anything for someone who brings me Mandel Bread," and he laughed. I told him about YPC and he said he had been reading about us and had enjoyed our Share 1 campaign. He chuckled saying he didn't own five houses so he didn't have to give us a million dollars. I told him about our development plan for urban projects in the next five years and that the boxes in New York City had brought in over three and a half million dollars. I wanted to start Cooperation House and The Lanes in Manhattan. "What are you going to buy with $3 ½ million dollars, a two bedroom apartment?" he asked ruefully. "Actually," I explained, "there are two large apartment buildings off Amsterdam in Harlem that have been vacant for years. They have a grassy lot between them, which we could turn into a little common area, and they could provide housing for a few hundred youth. I want to buy those two buildings, and I was hoping you could help me." We talked about the legal status of the buildings, who the owner was, and that YPC would cover all costs of renovation and offer them to 18-25 year olds who could not afford market rates in the City. The labor for the renovations, under the guidance of a construction company, would be provided by youth in the City, trained by YPC. It would be day labor, paid at the hourly rate of $10/hour, with a computerized list of the number of days each youth worked. As apartments were renovated, the youth with the most number of days worked would be able to live in them. He liked the idea. Then I dropped the fact that there was also some land located between East and West Harlem that could be perfect for The Lanes – Harlem. We would build it from the ground up. "That's mighty ambitious," he remarked. "Let's see what we can do." I told him that I had promises from two famous local musicians and one movie star to hold a concert to raise money for the purchase of the properties, if the Mayor was able to help us secure them.

"Dicho y hecho," (said and done) as the Spanish saying goes. The Mayor arranged a meeting with some city officials, the two property owners and three of us from YPC. We made verbal agreements on the purchase of the two locations and our respective lawyers would work out the details. The concert was to be held in Madison Square Garden three months hence and after that we would close the deals.

The day before I was returning to Miami, I popped into the Mayor's office to leave him another batch of Mandel Bread. I didn't expect to see him, but ran into him at his receptionist's desk. "Here you go, your stash," I joked. "Hey," he said, "You know your part of this bargain is to bring me Mandel Bread every time you're in New York." "Deal," I responded, "and I might even have my mother send you some from Kansas City." She'd love that.

Chapter 30

Calls from all over the world
and
Thank You, Bill Gates

We were hot! We were the rage. Everybody was talking about YPC. After the concert in Madison Square Garden, which commanded a full house, we were the cover story of Time Magazine. The cover was our logo on a light blue background and the words, "What is the Youth Peace Collective Showing the World?" The inside stories included a conversation between a reporter, three staff and three youth, an article about the Kansas City and Miami projects, another detailing what was proposed for New York and a beautiful pictorial section with text about our work in Ghana. They gave me the back page, and in a short essay entitled "Words from the Ground Up," I tried to lay out the practical and theoretical underpinnings of YPC.

Poor Florence was going insane at the headquarters office, a small space we rented on SW 27th Avenue, which she generally staffed by herself with occasional appearances by Ernie, Adrian, five new Miami staff, and me. She took on three full-time youth collective assistants and we added four phone lines. We were busy making plans for new regional urban projects to begin in a couple cities when representatives from the Palestinian Authority called, entreating us to make a visit there to see what fertile ground it would be for our project. I spoke to my friend Eva from Asuncion, Paraguay, whom I met in 1990 while she was working with a Catholic priest who provided street youth a chance to build their own living quarters. We hired her to do the groundwork for an irrigation project in the Paraguyan countryside. Staff quadrupled. Five new "Coordinators" were hired, from Israel, Palestine, Bolivia, Laos and Sudan, to start out as summer trainers and eventually go to different U.S. sites. Officials from the Philippines, Honduras, Niger, Burkina Faso (Ouagadougou is its capital: do you know where it is now? I'll give you a hint, it used to be called Upper Volta.), Haiti, Bolivia, South Africa and Brazil called us, all pleading for a meeting with some of our staff on their home turf.

Then one night I got a call at home around 11:00 p.m. I was sitting at my table painting peace boxes, my favorite relaxing activity. My stomach jumped when the phone rang and I looked at the clock. Must be somebody on the West Coast, I thought. Here's the conversation:

Me: Hello
Other Person, a male: Hello, may I please speak with Janet Zoglin.
Me: This is she.
Other Person: Hi, this is Bill Gates.
Me: Bill Gates? THE Bill Gates? Is this a joke?
BG: No, this is Bill Gates, I mean, my father and I are. In fact, I'm calling you because my father asked me to.
Me: Your father?
BG: Yeah, my father has been reading a lot about your youth peace group and he thinks we should get involved.

Me: Wow, that's great. It's fantastic. We'd be thrilled. What do *you* think about our work?
BG: Oh, it sounds really good, what I've read of it.

(Therein ensued a 45 minute conversation about our work, their work, theories on changing the world, etc.)

Me: You guys have done a lot of great work. Together we could make an incredible impact.
BG: We have computers we could offer you for all your different sites.
Me: Thank you.
BG: I'm not exactly sure what my father had in mind for our involvement. What would you like to see happen?
Me: There are so many ways we could work together. Doesn't it make sense to collaborate in developing countries, not just Africa, I mean, your work with disease eradication and ours with water technology?
BG: Sure. How shall we go about it?
Me: You give us money and we all start talking.

Two weeks later a check came in the mail from the Gates Foundation to YPC for one billion dollars. Thank you, generous Gates family, we'll be talking.

Chapter 31

Salaam Alekuum

The minute that check cleared I was on the horn to the Palestinian Authority. Stacey, Gail, Ernie, Khaled (new Palestinian staff), Avital (new Israeli staff) and I planned a visit. To join us, I invited Susan from S.F., a clinical psychologist and artist who had done a mural project with youth in the D'heisha refugee camp in 2001, and Danny and Sheya, my old friends from Kibbutz Hefzi-Ba, and Sheya's wife, Yasmin. We stayed three weeks. Oliver and James joined us for the last five days.

The first four days were spent in meetings; two days in Ramallah, two in Nablus. In various configurations, we met with Palestinian officials, Israeli officials, American officials, engineers, architects, construction companies, and manufacturers. "Houses with modern plumbing is what we need," said one Palestinian official. Another told us, "Clinics, doctors, and medical supplies." A third remarked, "We don't have playgrounds, libraries, recreation centers or anywhere for our children to go." During those sometimes conflictful, sometimes conciliatory encounters, we heard concerns, predicaments, mistrust, disbelief, and weary frustration. A prevailing sentiment finally emerged, "Let us attempt a new way." As an essential part of our fact-finding mission, the group expressed the desire to travel throughout Palestine, visiting cities, villages and refugee camps, talking to any and everybody. After that we would meet again for a final determination of the aspect of infrastructure YPC would undertake.

We were provided a large van, a bilingual driver named Ahmed, and encouraged to go anywhere and speak to whomever we wanted. Our first stop was the Jenin refugee camp. The "camps," started as precarious resettlement housing in tents, have now been around for 55 years. For this reason they no longer feel temporary, but rather like cramped conglomerations of human society, overcrowded and permanent. These days many houses in the camps are made from cinder blocks, some have flush toilets. Buildings often lean on each other, each dwelling smack up next to its neighbor, practically on top of one another. Following Ahmed, who occasionally called out to people along the way, we walked Jenin's narrow streets, where barely one car could pass. From the moment we set out we were constantly greeted by people who watched our group of ten walk by, "Salaam Alekuum," to which we replied, "Alekuum Salaam." (Peace unto you, and our, Unto you peace). Little kids came running up, chattering in Arabic. Everyone seemed so curious about us. Ernie called from the back of the group, "Hey Ahmed, what's all the rubble from?" Ahmed asked Khaled, "What's rubble?" "It's the trash, blocks and stones all around," Khaled explained. "Ern, that's from houses that have been knocked down. Sometimes when one house is torn down, the ones next to it also fall because they support each other." Avital said she knew that Israeli soldiers destroyed homes of families whose members had committed terrorist acts. Danny asked, "What do the people do when their home is gone?" Ahmed answered, "They move in with relatives, or into a tent until they can build another house." "Where? How?" I heard Stacey utter. On our stroll we saw graffiti everywhere. Mostly the writing was in

Arabic, but some was English. On one wall, next to a drawing depicting a soldier shooting someone, it said, "What did he do?" Often we would see representations of Handala, an outline in black of the back of a barefoot boy with a few strands of hair sticking straight out of his round head, hands crossed behind his back. "That's our Handala," Khaled said sadly. "He's like the Palestinian people, hurt on his head and his back. He represents a people that has been continuously mistreated." Here's how Handala looks:

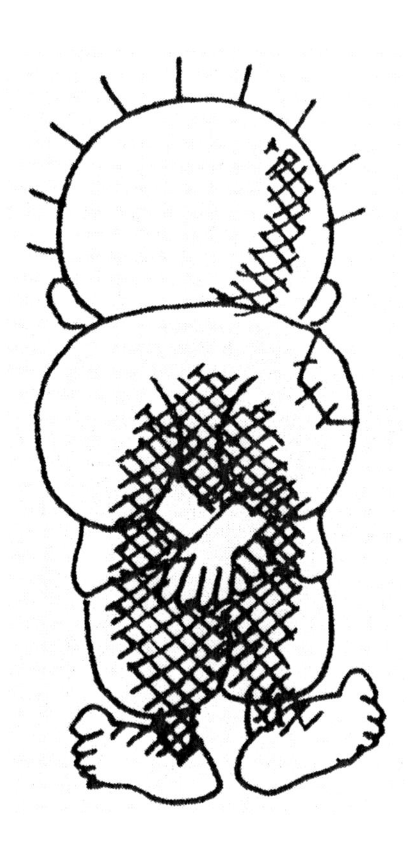

About forty minutes into our walk, a woman came out of her house, dressed in black with only her face showing, saying something emphatically to Ahmed and pointing to us. "This lady wants to invite you for tea – all of you." "Should we accept?" I asked. "Maybe it would be rude to decline, but there are an awful lot of us. I don't want to put her out." "Accept," he told me. "Go in there. Drink tea with her. And give me $20. There's something I'm going to try to bring to her house. Hopefully she will accept." Susan whispered, "Palestinians love to give, but they are very proud and it's hard for them to accept. I wonder what he's going to get." Ahmed yanked the sleeve of a man who had joined us walking and been chatting with Stacey and Gail. "Zakariya, you speak English. Go translate for them." Of course Khaled spoke both languages, but he was pleased to let the man, who looked around thirty, serve as our interpreter. "Zakariya is very respected in Jenin. His father was a martyr. It is good to be with him." Ahmed called out, rapidly walking away, turning a corner.

We entered the woman's three room house and positioned ourselves in the living room area. She had one low lying table in the center, a couch, two chairs, a bureau and rugs all around. She brought out tea and poured six glasses, then said something to Zakariya. "She says she has to make more, she will be just a minute. We sat silently, looking around. A calendar was on the wall, from 1999, with a picture of sunflowers. There was a large color print of the Dome of the Rock. A map of Palestine, which Zakariya stood up and looked at, then pointed to a spot, "This was where my family's village used to be." Two framed photographs, each of a young boy in school clothes, were on top of the bureau. One of them had a black cloth draped on it and a little Palestinian flag. Behind that photo, on the wall, was a white sheet with a full frontal face of that boy, a bit older and more serious, with writing like an announcement of some kind. Our hostess returned and poured six more glasses, for all of us and herself. Then she spoke what seemed like a prayer, because she bent her head. Zakariya translated, "She is thanking Allah for her life, her family, and for the visitors in her home." "Please tell her we thank her and wish a blessing for her and her family," Yasmin said. We picked up our tea and drank. It was sweet and strong. Just then Ahmed walked in with a big box, "Homemade pastries from my mother's cousin. She runs a little bakery, the best in Jenin." The woman laughed, "I will only let you bring those in because they come from a cousin of your family and I did not have time to make my own for our unexpected guests," Zakariya translated.

Khaled began speaking to the woman and they talked for a little while, the woman often gesturing to the photo with the black cloth on it. Khaled told us her youngest son had been shot by Israeli soldiers one day when tanks rolled down their street and he ran out with other boys to throw stones. He was 14 when he died. She said her other son, now 23, lived with her, but was not home at the moment and she hoped we would stay to meet him. Her husband had died four years before, from cancer. I asked Khaled to explain what YPC was hoping to do, and suggest that her older son might want to work with us. As he was relaying this information, she grew excited and kept repeating one particular word. "What's she saying?" Gail asked. "Work." Khaled replied. "She says how good that he will have work, because she depends on him, and that neither he nor any of his friends have work." Different members of our group threw questions at Zakariya and Khaled to ask the woman. "What do the people of Palestine need most?" Her response, "First, for the occupation to end." "What could the Youth Peace Collective create in Palestine to improve people's lives?" "We need a good system for water and to take away human waste. Sometimes here in the camp we only have water for one hour a day. You cannot live like a human being that way." "Do you think the young people will want to work with YPC?" To that question she turned her head and smiled, "Here's my son, why don't you ask him?" A thin young man with a gentle face had just walked in the room, a bit surprised to see his house full of foreigners. Zakariya greeted him, explained our presence and apparently told him quickly about YPC. Khaled asked if he and his friends would be interested in hearing more about the project. "Of course," he replied, glancing around the room. Then he, Khaled, Zakariya and Ahmed discussed the possibility of calling a meeting that very night of young people in the camp, males and females in our age range, to tell them about the project. The word went out, house to house, and that night a group of about 60 young adults gathered outside the mosque. The project principles were explained and again the questions were asked, what infrastructure development would be the most logical to begin with in Palestine? Would you yourself want to join YPC? Do you think the project is workable here? The youth said they needed jobs, that their people needed schools, accesssible water, medical facilities, more housing, community centers, places for the children to play. And yes, they were interested. From that group we asked for volunteers to be our guides the following day, that each one of us wanted to spend time with a group of three or four and go to different parts of the camp. Each guide group needed to consist of at least one person who spoke enough English to translate.

The next morning we went off with our groups, having our own individualized adventures, depending on what we asked our group to show us, or where they decided to take us. My group, two women (Taghreed and Mouna) and two men (Abdullah, and Ali) took me first to each of their family homes to meet their parents. In each house I was seated with the parents to drink tea, and served cookies or delicacies wrapped in grape leaves. Everyone had already heard about the project and uniformly they expressed an interest in their children participating. "Allah will bless you," Abdullah's father said, "for you are doing his work." Taghreed's mother asked whether all three of her daughters could join YPC, but one of the girls was only 16. I explained, through Ali who was my translator, about the age requirements, and informed them that the mother of the family would receive payments equal to the youth's at the end of training and each six-month term. Taghreed's mother took my hand, "Thank you, my sister. Do you know what that will do? It will bring some light into our lives. Our situation has been very desperate." We had decided that more than one youth per house could join – since there was nearly 100% unemployment among young adults, and many households contained multiple families. Also, it had been decided in our meetings during the first days, that Israeli youth would be invited to join YPC too. They would enter, if they were interested, after completing their military service. When we told Mouna's mother that Palestinian, Israeli, and American youth would be working together, learning the principles of building peace, she looked up in surprise. "Allah sees all." At Ali's house, his elderly grandmother came out and showed me a key. Ali explained, "My grandmother wants you to see the key to our house that was in the village. She has been keeping that key since 1948. She thinks that one day she will go back and open the door to her house. She doesn't know that where her house was is nothing but cactus now."

After the home visits, I asked my group to take me to the places where young people hang out. They consulted with each other and Ali translated, "You don't understand. There are no places for young people. The girls help their mothers. Some of us study. We go to the mosque." They took me to a two room building where I saw a children's art class in progress and heard singing from the other room. They showed me some schools, a couple of tea houses with only men inside, and an open yard where some boys were kicking a soccer ball around. "Mostly," Ali said, "we walk around and talk to each other, waiting to see what is going to happen. Nothing good has happened for a long time. We are tired and angry."

I sat with my group in a small restaurant, all of us drinking Coca Cola. We talked about the workshops and peace education component of YPC. I wondered how they felt about living and working collectively with Israeli youth. Abdullah remarked, "We don't really know each other. We have hated each other all our lives. We must learn to become friends." Taghreed commented that she hoped we would teach the men that women are important and of equal value in society. Mouna saw her friend Dina and asked her to come sit with us. Dina asked if the women would be carrying blocks and doing construction, just like the men. "That's the idea," I stated, wondering how it sounded to her. "What do you think of that?" " I'm not as strong as a man. I can't lift the heavy blocks," she told me. "Then we'll figure out what jobs the women can do, which ones feel appropriate and comfortable to them." I offered. "I will put the cement down," she laughed, "and cement to the ground the feet of any boy who says something to me I don't like. Do you think the Israeli boys will treat us with respect?" Respect was one of YPC's most fundamental concepts, I assured her.

At the end of the day we all met back outside the mosque. Ernie was sweating; he had just come from a basketball game with a group of young men. Stacey was carrying artwork she had bought when her group took her to various tiny artist studios. Gail said she had so many glasses of coffee she thought she would float away, and had eaten so much falafel, tabbouli, humus, and cous cous, she would never be hungry again. Khaled and his group had spent the afternoon in discussions with members of one of the militant groups. They had argued about the possibility of YPC's idea working. "The violence will not stop," they told him "until there is no more agression against us." Khaled tried to convince them, "Don't you see.

We are trying to work together, not fight against each other. We must all find a way to construct, not destruct." Avital had gone to see some women's cooperatives making crafts, to a bakery, a hospital and a children's daycare center. Danny had spent the day smoking cigarettes and drinking tea with a group of the oldest men in the camp. Sheya and Yasmin had walked with their group from house to house, greeting families and playing with little kids. Susan met with people in a community center and a school to talk about the possibility of starting mural projects. We told our guides that in one month YPC staff would be back with applications and we would begin interviewing youth. Oliver and James would be coming in a couple weeks to meet people, help in developing promotional materials, and begin structuring training sessions. Our young guides agreed to spread the word throughout the camp.

That night we all met for three hours and decided where we wanted to spend the next 10 days. We wanted to visit four more refugee camps, hold meetings and go on guided tours, as we had in Jenin. We hoped to have time to see Bethlehem, Gaza, Hebron, and spend two days in Jerusalem. Our intention was to put the word out as far and wide as we could, so when we returned, youth would be informed and ready to begin the application process. We also wanted to get a feel for life in the villages, and see the landscape of Palestine's countryside.

Immediately upon beginning our drive to Jabalia camp, we noticed well maintained highways connecting Israeli settlements to the main roads. Roads to

Palestinian settlements were rocky, winding, full of potholes and no wider than one lane. Ahmed explained that to get to some villages Palestinians had to take back roads that often took them hours out of their way, where once there had been a direct ten minute route. We passed many checkpoints. The countryside we saw was hilly, full of scrub and stones, shades of yellow and ochre. Some parts felt more like desert, other sectors had olive groves stretching for miles. Khaled pointed out one spot, "Look over there. Those trees are over 2000 years old." From the road, you could see villages nestled in the sloping, terraced hills. We visited a few of them, driving the circuitous routes to get there.

Driving in the van Ahmed shared stories of life in Palestine. He told us of his best friend's house being bulldozed because the father was suspected of being a terrorist. "That man was not a terrorist. He goes to the mosque every day and takes care of his family. But he had a Palestinian flag in his window." He said that once he finished secondary school, his family did not have money to send him to medical school, which was his dream, so he looked for any kind of work, but could never find any, until he was fortunate enough to get this job through one of his uncles as a part-time driver. "There is no work for our people. How are we to feed our families and make a life? If there is no work, there is no life." He told us how his sister had gotten married and had a baby, but her husband was injured in an automobile accident and could not work, so they had to move back with his family. "There are 8 of us living in a house with two bedrooms." He recounted what he said his grandfather always repeated to him, "We lived in our village at peace with the Israelis before 1948. We were friends. We traded with them. A man named Nachman from a kibbutz would exchange eggs and milk for my dates and olives. We would drink tea in each other's homes. Then one day we were told we had to leave, that our village was being demolished. My friend Nachman and I cried. I never saw him again." Ahmed was nearly in tears as he spoke of the time he took his grandfather back to the hill where their family house had been, now barren rocky land with scrub and cactus, and his grandfather fell to the ground and wailed on top of the ruins of steps which had led up to their front door.

In each of the camps, what we saw and what we heard was similar. We need work, larger houses, school supplies, medical services, clean running water. Our children need safe places to play and express creativity. In the van, leaving one of the camps, Sheya commented, "I find the Palestinian people very dignified, kind and generous." Danny added, "Many have expressed a sharp understanding of their situation. They feel a great injustice has been done to them." "Can we truly help?" Yasmin asked. Hours riding in the van were spent trying to answer that question.

It was not ours to comment on the political issues, nor did discussions of right and wrong in this long-standing, exceedingly complex dilemma seem helpful. We wished to offer opportunities to young Palestinians to improve their communities' living conditions. Danny, Sheya, Yasmin and Avital talked to us during our days together about how the situation has affected Israelis over the years, and of the divergent opinions on the topic which exist in Israeli society. "Haven't you ever heard it said," Yasmin asked, "If you have 12 Israelis in a room, you will have 13 opinions." In our talks to youth in Palestine we were finding it difficult to keep saying "YPC" or "Youth Peace Collective members," so Ahmed joked that we should refer to the youth as "Salaamniks" – something like the term "peaceniks," that was popular in the '60's. It caught on quickly, and I would hear Khaled giving a long speech in Arabic, interspersed with the word "Salaamnik," and the youth would smile. We wanted to represent belief in a possibility -- Salaam, Shalom, Peace, however you want to say it.

It was during our drives that we decided we wanted a staff comprised of seven American, seven Palestinian, and seven Israelis to begin managing the project. In the U.S. we would select three more staff to return with Stacey and Gail, while Avital and Khaled, along with James and Oliver, would be responsible for hiring colleagues from Palestine and Israel. Sheya,Yasmin, Zakariya, Ahmed, and Abdullah's older sister, a social worker, wanted to be part of the first staff group.

In Gaza we were cautioned about going in the ocean off the coast, because of unpredictably strong undertows. Tension in Bethlehem was perceptible, as we visited Christian holy sites. Hebron was a bustling city, with active markets. And everyone was awestuck as we walked the narrow, ancient alleyways of the old city of Jerusalem, talking to vendors in the market whose families had run those particular stands for 600 years. One afternoon we visited the Church of the Holy Sepulchre, the Wailing Wall, and the Dome of the Rock – holiest sites of three main religions, all located a short walking distance from each other. Jewish Quarter. Muslim Quarter. Armenian Quarter. Christian Quarter. Huge wooden doors at the gates to keep out invaders in the olden days. It was all so intertwined. I must have drunk seven bottles of "mitz eshcoliot" – grapefruit juice drink – as I would take a moment to sit down somewhere in the shade, contemplating the thousands of years of history beneath my feet. Something spiritual was in the wind. I can't explain it.

We took two days off – I went to Tel Aviv with Ahmed to pick up James and Oliver, then to Jericho. Avital took Gail and Khaled to her family's house in Haifa. Ernie went to the Dead Sea, and Stacey, Susan, Danny, Sheya and Yasmin went to Safed, the Sea of Galilee and to see Hefzi-Ba and it's neighboring kibbutz, Beit Alpha. We reunited in Ramallah in the office of the Palestinian official who had first contacted YPC. "Well, what do you think?" he inquired. "Where do we begin?" "They want to turn our youth into a bunch of Salaamniks," Khaled blurted. I started to say something, but Khaled continued, "The youth are interested." Avital added, "We are interested as well." "You will have our full cooperation," the official said. "An orchard begins by planting the first tree."

We presented our proposal. To start out we wanted to construct in each refugee camp and highly populated city a large building to be called "Beit Salaam," (Peace House). They would be three stories, with the first floor a library/cafe, run by YPC youth. The second floor would be a medical clinic, with waiting rooms, doctor's offices, examination rooms and facilities for basic tests and labwork. The third floor would be classrooms where a variety of artistic, craft, and musical workshops would take place. Each building would have a garden area with basketball courts and children's playground equipment. In our first year of work, while Peace Houses were going up, we would begin extensive meetings, negotiations and planning to bring potable water to the whole of Palestine. Water, symbolically and practically, seemed a key. Would we be able to open the lock? The building of houses would not begin until year three or four, but in the meantime the belief was that many families would be able to construct or enlarge dwellings with the significant payments YPC intended to make to youth and their mothers.

Ernie, Khaled and a Palestinian lawyer we hired would begin drawing up contracts for large-scale purchases of concrete blocks, cement, plumbing fixtures, wooden tables and chairs, roofing and other construction materials. I had asked Tina to look for medical supplies and equipment donations in the States. Maybe we could get the NBA to supply us with basketball goals. Besides staff selection, Khaled and Avital would be translating all informational materials into Arabic and Hebrew. We realized that the very first group of youth would have to have a basic working knowledge of English, but we would be figuring out a system of simultaneous translation and/or introductory English classes to open up access to all youth. My cousin in San Diego who is an expert in teaching English as a second language, will want to come and help, I'm sure.

In two months I intended to return with a group of trainers to do a month of workshops for the first Palestinian and Israeli entrants, who by then would have been selected. American YPC members would arrive during the last week of the session. We had been offered the site of an abandoned monastery to initially use as our peace training location, and tented camps would be created at different sites as Beit Salaam construction began. All I kept dreaming about was going to the homes of each and every youth who was accepted into YPC, having tea or coffee with their parents, and thanking them individually for allowing their children to join us in this endeavor. I wanted to bring a handmade peace box for each family too – surely they would accept that.

Alekuum Salaam.

Chapter 32

The End
and
The Future

"When is this story going to end?" Oliver asked me. Right now, my friends. I'll close by telling you what happened the next five years in YPC, and then you're on your own.

Year Three was the year of "P's." Besides our work in Palestine, we renovated and turned old hotels into Cooperation Houses in Philadelphia and Portland (Oregon), and began laying plumbing and irrigation tubing in Paraguay. We bought the Tower Hotel and surrounding properties (a personal triumph) and became our own 501 (c)(3), still working closely with Storytellers. Various members of the Walton Family (as in WalMart) donated millions of dollars to a scholarship fund at Antioch for Youth Peace Collective graduates. That year mainland Equatorial Guinea (Africa's only Spanish-speaking country) experienced disastrous floods, causing tremendous loss of property and infrastructure. The entire YPC group from Ghana flew there for two months to help the "damnificados" (affected individuals) and we began a project for clean running water, training and including inYPC every interested local youth between 18-25. Our work helped those families rebuild their demolished lives and gave an economic jolt to this depressed and abandoned former colonial paradise in West Africa, whose capital is on an island off the Cameroonian coast.

Year Four was the "A" year. We opened up The Lanes in Atlanta, Albuquerque, Akron, and Cooperation House in Oakland. Water projects were begun in Afghanistan, and Algeria. Our World Headquarters construction commenced. We held an All -YPC music competition for original compositions only, about peace. Any music style was accepted, by individuals or groups. The judges were: Lauryn Hill, Bono, Mos Def, Lucinda Williams, Youssou N'Dour, Miriam Makeba, Hassan Hakmoun and Shakira. The song that won the Grand Prize of $5,000, a lively tune with background chorals called "Realizing Peace," was a collaborative effort by two Americans from Mississippi and two Ghanaian youth. Second place, receiving $2,500, was a lovely ballad called "We are bringing peace to your hearts" written and performed on acoustic guitar by a young woman from San Antonio. And third place, $1,000, went to a rap group comprised of a New Yorker, a Palestinian, and a kid from Des Moines. Their song was called "We're going to put an end to war, Bro." Bono, stating that many of the competition songs were "incredible," produced a C.D. with twelve of the submissions, titled: "YPC – Realizing Peace." We won the Grammy that year, in the category of Best New Artist, though they never knew exactly what genre to place us in. Myriam and Bono accepted the award; their acceptance speech was saying together, "Thank you. Peace," holding up their two fingers in the peace sign.

Year Five we instituted a new urban project called "YPC Family Helpers," originally foster mom cousin's idea. It was an excellent new employment option because it incorporated large numbers of youth, had very little overhead, and provided a greatly needed service. YPC members would go into homes where our help had been requested and babysit, shop, clean house, mediate between parents and children, and in general relieve stressed out family members by doing whatever (reasonable) tasks they needed. Youth received training and were set up with schedules, similar to visiting physical therapists, with different clients on different days. That year we set up over 20 family helper offices throughout the U.S. We also built a factory in Burkina Faso that made irrigation tubing, and one in Malawi that produced a new kind of toilet, designed by a YPC engineer. Each of these factories gave "product" free to YPC, and sold the rest of their production on the open market. They were set up as collectives, owned and operated by the workers. Haiti and Honduras started water projects.

Year Six was the year of the big bowling competition. We had a countrywide tournament, offering hefty first prize money and all-expense paid trips for two to Paris, London and Buenos Aires for 2nd, 3rd and 4th runners up . We had begun buying bowling alleys that were suffering financially and turning them into The Lanes – Baltimore, San Diego, Houston, Fargo, Cleveland, New Orleans, Boston, Los Angeles, and Boise. The competition lasted three months, and was often covered in local newspaper's sports page. The final round was bowled at The Lanes Northeast and the winner was a 6' 4" 300 pound young man from Columbia, South Carolina. That year we formed a close working relationship with AMF bowl, and helped them out of their economic doldrums. By this time we had 127 YPC graduates, American and foreign, enrolled at

Antioch College. Bolivia and Bosnia started irrigation projects.

And Year Seven we began planting "Tea Tree," aloe, and hemp in various countries around the world. Tea Tree Oil is a natural antispetic, quite effective when placed on bug bites, cuts and scrapes; aloe helps burns and many other conditions, internal and external. Next to each large plantation, in four countries, we built bottling plants and worldwide marketing was carried out from there. Hemp fields sprang up in 22 countries. As you may know, hemp is a durable substance for building materials, rope, paper, and clothing, as well as producing an oil used for the skin, hair and cooking. It is also an excellent plant to regenerate soil devastated by deforestation or flooding, and can grow in nearly every climate. Clothing was manufactured in three locations, and products under the name of "Hempeace," designed and produced by youth collective members, were sweeping the market. From that point on, YPC t-shirts were always made of hemp. A hemp building material, sturdier than sheetrock, was developed and factories were being constructed to manufacture it in Borneo, Colombia, Vietnam, Brazil, Liberia, and Uganda. An interesting statistic emerged that year: U.S. military enrollment was down 67%, thus the armed services were closing a number of bases and putting them up for sale. We bought five, and began working on a plan to offer every youth in America the chance to do one year of "peace service" some time between ages of 18 and 25.

There it is, dear readers, the future now entirely open – for peace.

Printed in the United States
1475600001B/172-210